Revision Exercise 1a

1 (a) Number cards are arranged to make the number 4791

4	7	9	1

(i) What is the value of the 7 in this number?

Answer _____

(ii) Write this number to the nearest 100.

Answer _____

(iii) Rearrange the cards to make the largest number possible.

Answer

(b) Write down the number six thousand and twenty-five.

Answer _____

2 (a) Write down the next two terms in the sequence:
7, 13, 19, 25, ….., ….,

Answer _____ and _____

(b) (i) Continue the sequence of shapes made from matchsticks to show the fourth shape.

Shape 1   Shape 2   Shape 3   Shape 4

(ii) Complete the following table showing the number of matchsticks which make each of the first 5 shapes.

Number of Shape	1	2	3	4	5
Number of matchsticks	3	5	7		

(iii) What is the rule for the pattern of the number of matchsticks being used?

Answer _____

3 (a) Mark a point X on the circumference of the circle drawn below.

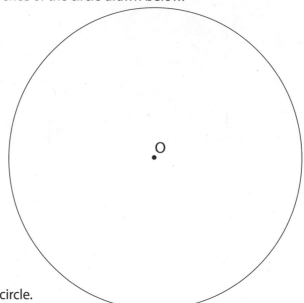

(b) Join X to O at the centre of the circle.

(i) What is the line OX called?

Answer _____

(ii) Measure the length of OX.

Answer _____ cm

4 The bar chart shows the **average daily temperatures** in Spain from April to October.

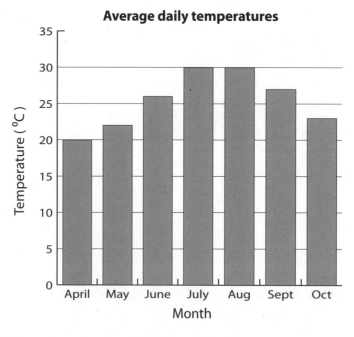

(a) Which two months have the same average daily temperature?

Answer _____ and _____

(b) Which month has the lowest average daily temperature?

Answer _____

(c) What is the **range** for the average daily temperatures?

Answer _____

5 (a) From the numbers 11, 49, 15, 21, 33, 6, 7 write down

    (i) a square number

                                                        Answer _____

    (ii) a multiple of 5

                                                        Answer _____

    (iii) a factor of 54

                                                         Answer _____

(b) George has £5. He buys 4 packets of stickers at 60p each.
    How much change should he get?
    Show your working

                                                        Answer £ _____

Revision Exercise 2a

1

37	42	89
17	50	73
11	67	12

From the numbers in the above grid

(a) write down the **two** numbers which total 100

Answer _____ and _____

(b) write down the **two** numbers which differ by 50

Answer _____ and _____

(c) find the **greatest** number you can make by multiplying **two** numbers

Answer _____

2 (a)

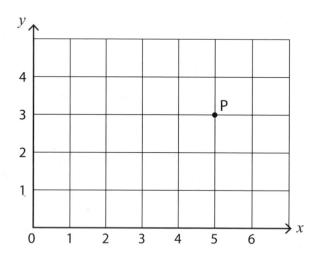

Write down the co-ordinates of the point P.

Answer (_____ , _____)

(b) Find the next two terms in the sequence

5, 9, 13, 17, ... , ...,

Answer _____ and _____

3

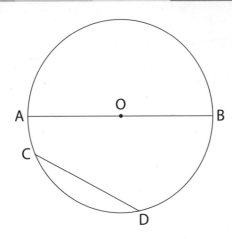

Choose from

chord	circumference	radius
diameter	tangent	

to complete these sentences:

(a) The line AOB is called a _____.

(b) The line CD is called a _____.

4 (a) What metric unit would be used to measure:

  (i) the length of a school corridor?

Answer _____

  (ii) the amount of nail polish in a bottle?

Answer _____

(b)

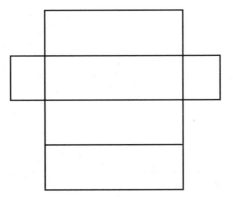

The diagram shows the net of a shape. Name the shape.

Answer _____

5 (a)

    (i) Write 0.602, 0.620 and 0.062 in ascending order.

Answer _____

    (ii) Convert 1.2 metres to milimetres.

                                                         Answer _____ mm

(b) From the list of test results

    8, 5, 6, 8, 7, 4, 7, 8, 5, 9, 8, 2, 9, 7, 8

    find:

    (i) the mode

                                                           Answer _____

    (ii) the median

                                                           Answer _____

(c) Michael scored 62% in a Maths test. The median for Michael's class was 64%.
    Describe how well Michael did.

Answer _____

_____

_____

_____

Revision Exercise 3a

1 75 people were asked which music they liked best. The first three rows of the pictogram are drawn below.

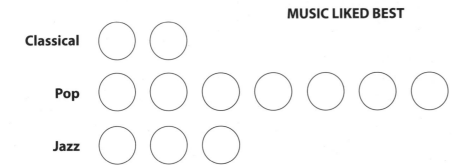

MUSIC LIKED BEST

Classical

Pop

Jazz

Other

(a) 10 people liked **Classical** music best.

Complete the key: ◯ = _____ people

(b) How many people liked **Pop** music best?

Answer _____

(c) Complete the row of the pictogram for **Other** music.

2 A tourist is facing in the direction of a tower which is due North of him.

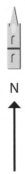

N

(a) He makes a $\frac{1}{4}$ turn clockwise. In what direction is he now facing?

Answer _____

(b) He makes a further $\frac{1}{2}$ turn clockwise. In what direction is he now facing?

Answer _____

(c) How much further clockwise does he need to turn to face North again?

Answer _____

3 (a) Mary's grandpa was 79 years old on 12 September 2008. In what year was he born?

Answer _____

(b) Write down all the factors of 18

Answer _____

(c) 400 tickets were printed for a Bangor Ladies' Choir concert.
127 tickets remain to be sold. How many are sold?

Answer _____

4

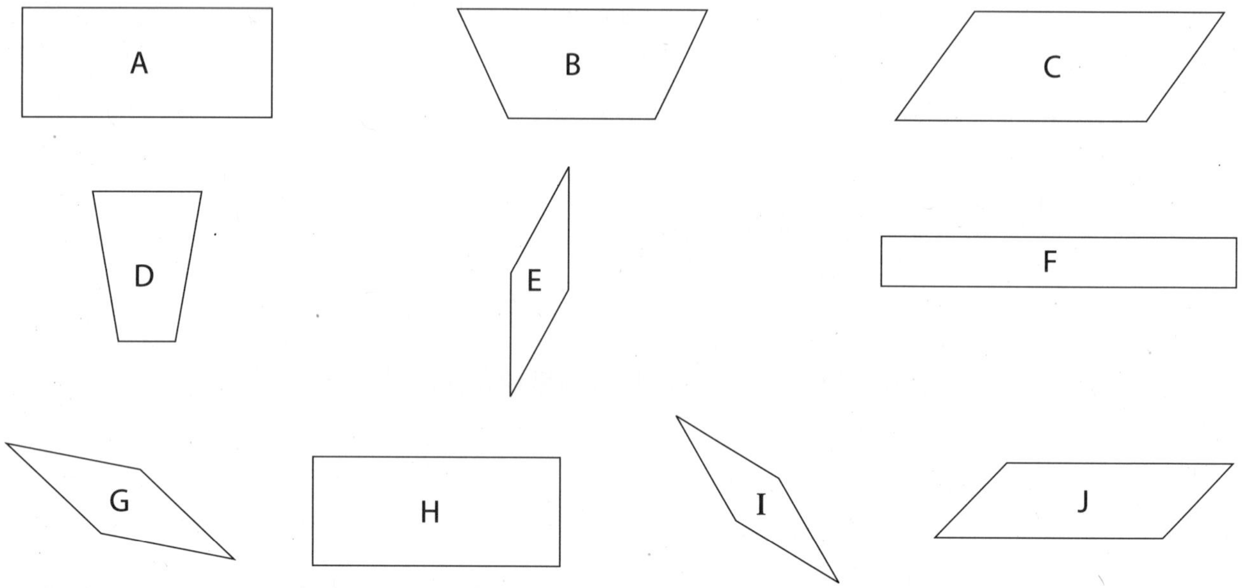

A   B   C

D   E   F

G   H   I   J

(a) Name two pairs of congruent shapes.

Answer _____ and _____

Answer _____ and _____

(b) Choose from

square	rhombus	rectangle	kite
trapezium	pentagon	parallelogram	

to complete the sentences.

(i) Shape A is a _____

(ii) Shape B is a _____

(iii) Shape C is a _____

5

A  B

(a) Measure the length of the line AB.

Answer AB = _____

(b) Using AB as the base, construct a triangle ABC. The length of AC is 6 cm and CAB is a right angle.

(c) Measure the length of the line BC.

Answer BC = _____

6

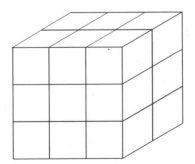

The cuboid is made up of 1 cm cubes. What is the volume of the cuboid?

Answer _____ cm³

Revision Exercise 4a

1 Pupils choose the following to drink at break time.

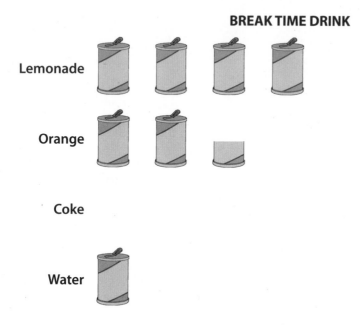

BREAK TIME DRINK

Lemonade

Orange

Coke

Water

(a) 16 pupils choose lemonade. Complete the scale key.

means _____ pupils

(b) How many pupils choose orange?

Answer _____ pupils

(c) 24 pupils choose coke. Complete the pictogram.

2 (a) 1250 mm are cut from a 2 m length of skirting board. What length is left?

Answer _____ mm

(b) 492 eggs are packed into cartons. Each carton holds 6 eggs.
How many cartons will be needed?

Answer _____

(c) Write 32 out of 200 as a percentage.

Answer _____ %

3 (a) Write the following in ascending order:

(i) $\frac{1}{3}$, $\frac{1}{2}$, $\frac{1}{5}$

Answer _____

(ii) 2, −5, 0

Answer _____

(b) Find the next two terms in the sequence:

13, 10, 7, 4, …., ….,

Answer _____ and _____

4 (a)

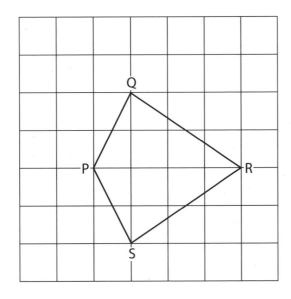

(i) Find the area of PQRS.

Answer _____ squares

(ii) Name the shape PQRS.   *Answer* _____

(b) Find the perimeter of the shape below, made from 1 cm squares.

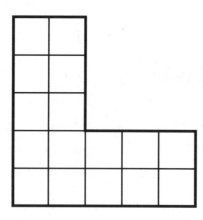

Answer _____ cm

5 O is the centre of the circle drawn below.

(Diagram not drawn to scale)

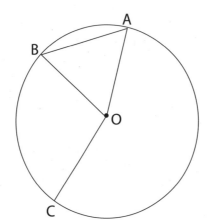

(a) Choose from

acute	**isosceles**	**scalene**
obtuse	**perpendicular**	**right angled**

to complete the sentences.

(i) Angle BOC is

Answer _____

(ii) Angle AOB is

Answer _____

(b) If OAB is 60° then what type of triangle is AOB?

Answer _____

Revision Exercise 1b

1 (a) Continue this sequence of shapes made from square tiles to show the fourth shape.

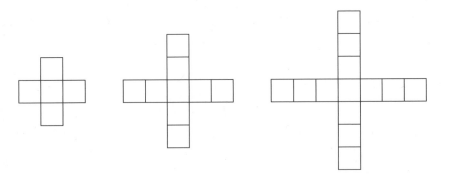

Shape1   Shape 2   Shape 3   Shape 4

(b) Complete the following table showing the number of square tiles to make each of the first 5 shapes.

Number of shape	1	2	3	4	5
Number of square tiles	5	9	13		

(c) What is the rule for the number of square tiles being used for each shape?

Answer _____

(d) How many square tiles would it take to make shape 9?

Answer _____

2 (a)   Circle the fractions in the list that are **not** equal to $\frac{1}{4}$?

$\frac{2}{8}$, $\frac{4}{12}$, $\frac{5}{20}$, $\frac{7}{28}$, $\frac{8}{40}$

(b) Write $\frac{2}{5}$, 0.5, 30% in ascending order.

Show your working

*Answer*_____ , _____ , _____

3 (a) Solve the equations

   (i) $7x = 21$

   Answer _____

   (ii) $x + 5 = 13$

   Answer _____

(b) Simplify $3a + a + 6a$

   Answer _____

(c) Expand
   $3(x + 5)$

   Answer _____

4 Fifteen pupils estimated the size of an angle drawn on a page. The information is shown in a stem and leaf diagram.

Angle Estimates

```
5 | 1 1 3
4 | 2 2 6 6 6 8
3 | 1 3 4 7
2 | 7 9
```

$2 | 7$ means $27°$

(a) What is the largest estimate?

   Answer _____

(b) What estimate is the mode?

   Answer _____

(c) What estimate is the median?

   Answer _____

(d) The size of the angle is $47°$. How many pupils estimated less than the size of the angle?

   Answer _____ pupils

5 The diagram shows the position of a troop of soldiers and their base.
In what direction is the base from the troop of soldiers?

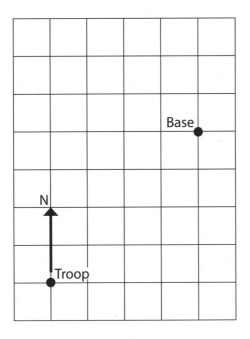

Answer _____

6 (a) *Dancing on Ice the Skate Off* starts at 8.50 pm. What is this time on a 24 hour clock?

Answer _____

(b) Write 80% as a decimal.

Answer _____

(c) Write 17 out of 20 as a percentage.

Answer _____ %

(d) Calculate
    (i) 7% of £800

Answer _____

    (ii) 70% of £50

Answer _____

Revision Exercise 2b

1 A multiple choice paper is marked as follows:

3 marks for a correct answer (✔)
−2 marks for an incorrect answer (✘)
−1 mark when there is no attempt to answer a question (−)

CLAIRE'S ATTEMPT

Question Number	1	2	3	4	5	6	7	8	9	10
	✔	✔	✘	✘	−	✔	−	✔	✘	✔
Marks	3	3	−2	−2	−1					

(a) Complete the table of marks and find Claire's score.

Answer _____

(b) John scored −2.

(i) How many marks difference is there between John's score and Claire's score?

Answer _____

(ii) John got no questions incorrect. How many did he attempt?

Answer _____

(iii) Describe another way to score −2.

Answer _____

_____

2

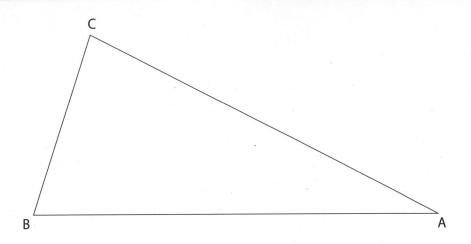

(a) Measure the angle B

Answer _____ °

(b)

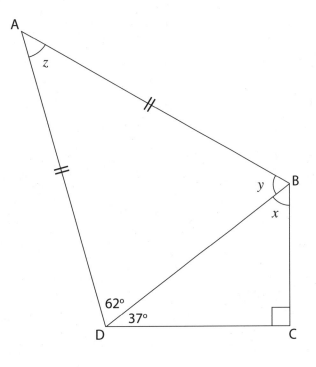

Diagram *not* accurately drawn

ABD is an isosceles triangle with AB = AD.
BCD is a right angled triangle.

Calculate the size of angle:

(i) x

Answer _____ °

(ii) y

Answer _____ °

(iii) z

Answer _____ °

3 (a) Calculate

(i) 8^2

Answer _____

(ii) $\sqrt{49}$

Answer _____

(iii) 5^3

Answer _____

(b) Write $\frac{5}{8}$ as a percentage.

Answer _____ %

4 (a) Solve the equations:

(i) $19 - x = 14$

Answer _____

(ii) $\frac{x}{4} = 8$

Answer _____

(iii) $4x - 3 = 9$

Answer _____

(b) Expand
$3(2x + 5)$

Answer _____

5 (a) Calculate

(i) $\frac{1}{4} + \frac{1}{8}$

Answer _____

(i) $\frac{1}{2} - \frac{1}{6}$

Answer _____

(b) At 6 am the temperature in New York is −7° C. At mid-day it is 1° C.
By how much has the temperature risen?

Answer _____ ° C

6 (a) Kevin bought a magazine costing £1.55 and a bottle of cola costing £1.08

(i) What was the total cost of the two items?

Answer _____

(ii) How much change did he get from £5?

Answer _____

(b) Write down
(i) the value of the cube root of 27,

Answer _____

(ii) both values of the square root of 36.

Answer _____ , _____

Revision Exercise 3b

1

	Antrim	Armagh	Belfast	Downpatrick	Enniskillen	Larne	Derry	Omagh
Armagh	42							
Belfast	18	41						
Downpatrick	37	47	22					
Enniskillen	86	50	84	94				
Larne	21	63	22	44	106			
Derry	54	71	72	93	61	75		
Omagh	54	37	70	80	27	75	34	
Portrush	46	68	63	84	98	55	39	72

Distance in miles

(a) Which two towns are the greatest distance apart?

Answer ______________________ and ______________________

(b) The distance from Belfast to Enniskillen is 84 miles. Which other two towns are 84 miles apart?

Answer ______________________ and ______________________

(c) Jean drives from Armagh to Enniskillen and back to Armagh. How many miles is this?

Answer ______________ miles

2 (a) (i) Write down the value of $2790 \div 10$

Answer ______________

(ii) What is the value of 7 in the number 67 451?

Answer ______________

(b) Write down the value of

(i) 9^2

Answer ______________

(ii) $\sqrt{64}$

Answer ______________

3 (a) Solve the equation

$$3x + 7 = 19$$

Answer $x =$ _____

(b) Write down the next two terms in the sequence

13 , 9, 5, 1, ...

Answer _____ and _____

(c) Expand

$$-5(x + 2)$$

Answer _____

4 (a) Calculate

(i) $\frac{2}{3} + \frac{1}{4}$

Answer _____

(ii) $\frac{3}{4} - \frac{1}{10}$

Answer _____

(b) The price of a laptop is £300 + £60 VAT.
What is the VAT percentage rate?

Answer _____ %

5 (a) Simplify $3a - 2b - b + 7a$

Answer _____

(b) Solve $17 - x = 9$

Answer _____

6 (a) (i) Write 6.27638 correct to two decimal places.

Answer _____

  (ii) Write down the largest of these numbers.

   0.217   0.2673   0.29

Answer £_____

(b) Mary bought 4 packets of chewing gum at 38p each.

 (i) How much in total did the 4 packets cost?

Answer £_____

 (ii) How much change did she get from £5?

Answer _____

(c) What decimal is equivalent to $\frac{5}{100}$?

Answer _____

7 (a) Simplify

  $4a + 5b - a - 3b$

Answer _____

(b) Expand

  $x(x - 3)$

Answer _____

Revision Exercise 4b

1 Plot the points (2 , -1) and (-3 , 0).

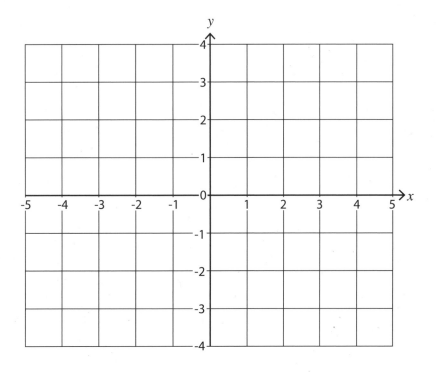

2 (a) Calculate the volume of a cuboid with dimensions 5 cm, 6 cm and 8 cm.

Answer _____ cm³

(b) Another cuboid has the same volume as this one. The area of its base is 80 cm². What is its height?

Answer _____ cm

3 From the list of numbers

21, 32, 47, 81, 63, 16, 95, 79, 15

write down:

(a) two prime numbers,

Answer _____ and _____

(b) a cube number.

Answer _____

4 Draw a net of the prism shown.

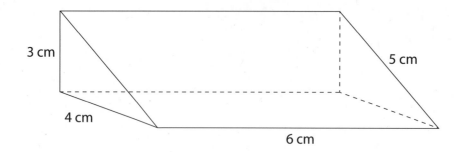

5 (a)

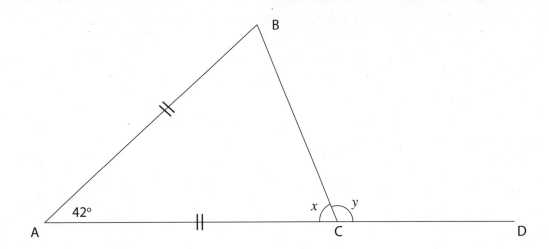

ACD is a straight line.
AB = AC

Calculate the size of angle:

(i) x

Answer $x =$ _____ °

(ii) y

Answer $y =$ _____ °

(b)

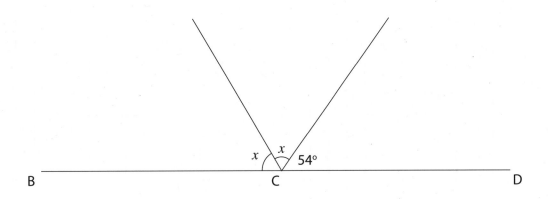

BCD is a straight line.
Calculate the value of x

Answer $x =$ _____ °

6 An athletic's coach recorded a sprinter's finishing position in her last 36 races.

Position	1st	2nd	3rd	4th	5th
Frequency	2	5	7	10	12

Draw a bar chart to show this information.

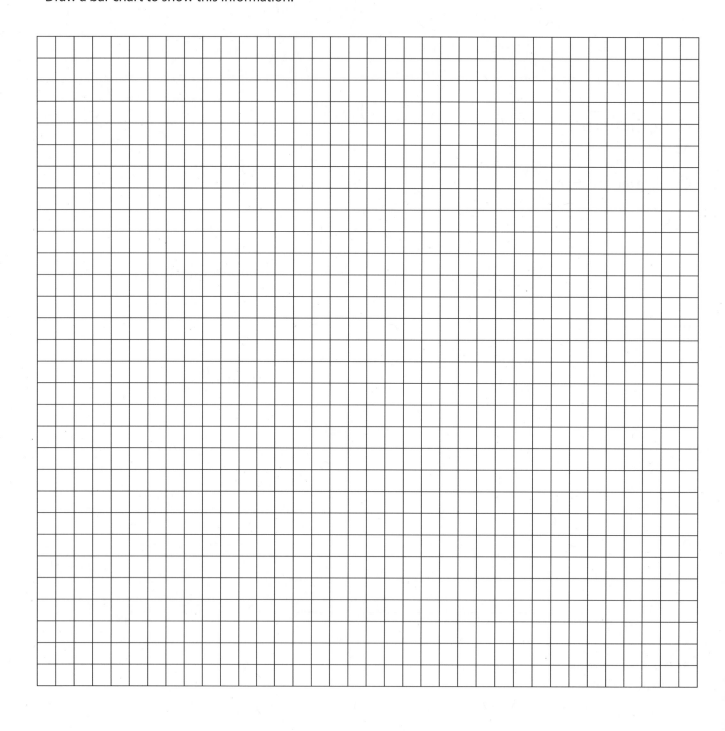

Revision Exercise 1c

1 (a) Complete the following shopping bill.

2.5 kg new potatoes at 84p per kg   _____

3 litres of milk at £1.05 per litre   _____

0.25 kg tomatoes at £1.64 per kg   _____

Total £   _____

(b) £10 is used to pay for the shopping. What is the change?

Answer £_____

(c) 1 saver point is awarded for each £1 spent. How many saver points are earned when buying these 3 items?

Answer _____

2

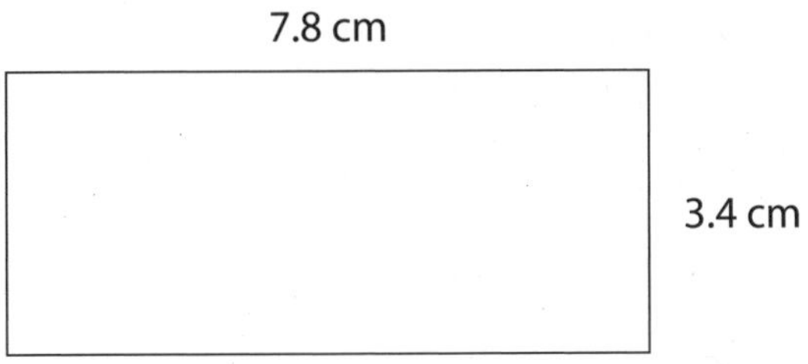

7.8 cm

3.4 cm

(a) Find the area of the rectangle drawn above.

Answer _____ cm^2

(b) Find the perimeter of the rectangle drawn above.

Answer _____ cm

3 (a) Find
   (i) $\sqrt{2.25}$

   Answer _____

   (ii) 3.3^2

   Answer _____

(b) Calculate
   $2.9^2 - 3.5$

   Answer _____

(c) An iPod is priced at £150. In a sale, 20% discount is given.

   How much is the discount?

   Answer £ _____

4 (a) The cost of hiring a carpet cleaner is £15.75 plus £4.25 per day.
   How much does it cost to hire the carpet cleaner for 3 days?

   Answer £ _____

(b) Another hire company charges £22.75 for the first day and £2.25 for each additional day.
   Mrs Todd pays £34 for the hire of the carpet cleaner.

   For how many days did she hire this carpet cleaner?

   Answer _____days

5 (a) Lorraine pays £1.75 for 0.4 kg of green grapes and 0.5 kg of black grapes. The green grapes cost £1.85 per kg.

   How much are the black grapes per kg?

   Answer £ _____

(b) Myla earns £14000 per year. On 1 April 2008 she is due to get a 3% pay rise.

   How much is this pay rise per year?

   Answer £ _____

6 As an incentive to use a credit card 1 *UR-point* is awarded for each 50p spent.
Neil's use of his credit card has earned him 27077 *UR-points*.
He investigates using them to pay for return flights to London for his wife and himself.

(a) If they take 2 suitcases 33100 *UR-points* are required
  (i) How many *UR-points* does he still need to collect?

Answer _____

  (ii) How much does this require him to spend using his credit card?

Answer £_____

(b) If they take only 1 suitcase then 25900 *UR-points* are required.
How many *UR-points* are saved by taking only 1 suitcase?

Answer _____

(c) Using money it costs £18 to take a suitcase.
How many *UR-points* are equivalent to £1?

Answer _____

Revision Exercise 2c

1 Some teenagers were asked the type of movie they liked best.
The results are shown below.

Horror	20%
Action	35%
Comedy	25%
Love	5%
Science Fiction	15%

Use the circle to draw a pie chart to show this information.

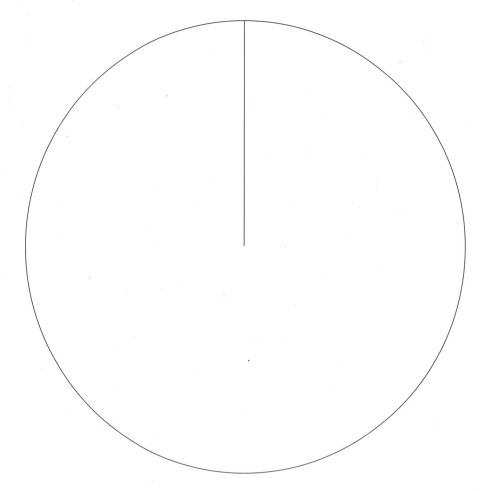

2 Oil cost 50p per litre when Mrs Gaw last bought 900 litres. Since then, the price of oil has gone up by 8%.
She is due a delivery of 900 litres.

How much should she expect to pay for it?

Answer £ _____

3 On holiday Siobhan is looking for some souvenirs to bring home to her friends.
She spots some fridge magnets at 85p each.

(a) How many can she buy for £10?

Answer _____

(b) How much change should she get?

Answer _____

4 (a) A bowling club has 56 members. Thirty five of these are men.
What fraction are men?
Give your answer in its lowest terms.

Answer _____

(b) A school has 300 pupils. On Friday 270 pupils were present.
What percentage was present?

Answer _____ %

(c) A jug contains 500 ml of juice. $\frac{1}{5}$ of the juice is poured into a glass and $\frac{1}{4}$ of the juice is poured into another glass.

What fraction of juice is left in the jug?
Give your answer in its lowest terms.

Answer _____

5 Parts of an Electricity Bill are shown below.

Balance at previous bill	– £ 76.91
Payments received up to 1 February 2011	£207.00

(a) Calculate the amount in credit at 1 February 2011.

Answer __£_____

(b)

Meter reading date	Present Reading	Previous Reading	Units Used	Units Price (pence)	Tariff Description
21 February 2008	57105	54742		11.02	Home Energy

(i) Complete the table above for the number of units used.

(ii) Calculate the cost to the nearest penny of the units used.

Answer £ _____

(c) The cost of the units used by Mr and Mrs Luke is £160.

Calculate the

(i) VAT at 5% on the cost of the units used,

Answer £ _____

(ii) total cost of the electricity used including the VAT.

Answer £ _____

6 (a) Mrs Jay shares paying the bills with her husband.
She sets up the following monthly direct debits from her bank account.

Electricity	£35.00
Rates	£67.54
TV Licence	£14.55
TV, broadband and phone	£44.00
Car insurance	£42.23
Heating oil	£80.00

What is the total cost of these direct debits?

Answer £ _____

(b) Each month her take home pay is £1066.37
She saves £150 and puts aside £80 for petrol and £320 to buy food.
How much is left over for spending on other things?

Answer £ _____

ANSWERS

Exercise 1a
1 (a) (i) 7 hundred **(ii)** 4800 **(iii)** 9741 **(b)** 6025

2 (a) 31, 37 **(b) (i)** 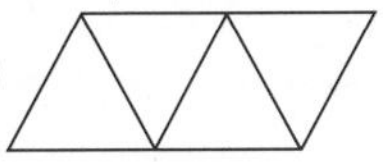 **(ii)** 9, 11 **(iii)** Goes up in twos, or odd numbers starting with 3

3 (a) point X marked anywhere on the circumference. **(b) (i)** radius **(ii)** 4 ± 0.2 cm
4 (a) July and August **(b)** April **(c)** 10° C
5 (a) (i) 49 **(ii)** 15 **(iii)** 6 **(b)** £2.60

Exercise 2a
1 (a) 11 and 89 **(b)** 17 and 67 **(c)** 6497
2 (a) (5, 3) **(b)** 21, 25
3 (a) diameter **(b)** chord
4 (a) (i) metres **(ii)** ml **(b)** pyramid
5 (a) (i) 0.062, 0.602, 0.620 **(ii)** 1200 mm **(b) (i)** 8 **(ii)** 7 **(c)** In the bottom half of the class

Exercise 3a
1 (a) Key: 5 people **(b)** 35 **(c)** 3 circles drawn opposite 'Other'
2 (a) East **(b)** West **(c)** $\frac{1}{4}$ turn or 90°
3 (a) 1929 **(b)** 1, 2, 3, 6, 9, 18 in any order **(c)** 273
4 (a) A and H; E and I **(b) (i)** Rectangle **(ii)** Trapezium **(iii)** Parallelogram
5 (a) 8 cm **(b)** accurate right angled triangle at A **(c)** 10 cm ± 1 mm
6 18 cm³

Exercise 4a
1 (a) Key: 4 pupils **(b)** 10 **(c)** 6 cans drawn opposite 'Coke'
2 (a) 750 mm or 0.75 m **(b)** 82 **(c)** 16 %
3 (a) (i) $\frac{1}{5}$, $\frac{1}{3}$, $\frac{1}{2}$ **(ii)** -5, 0, 2
4 (a) (i) 8 **(ii)** Kite **(b)** 20 cm
5 (a) (i) Obtuse **(ii)** Acute **(b)** Equilateral

Exercise 1b
1 (a) Shape drawn with one extra square added to each of the 4 arms. **(b)** 17, 21 **(c)** goes up in fours **(d)** 37
2 (a) $\frac{4}{12}$ and $\frac{8}{40}$ circled **(b)** 30%, $\frac{2}{5}$, 0.5
3 (a) (i) 3 **(ii)** 8 **(b)** 10a **(c)** 3x + 15
4 (a) 53° **(b)** 46° **(c)** 42° **(d)** 11
5 NE
6 (a) 2050 **(b)** 0.8 **(c)** 85% **(d) (i)** £56 **(ii)** £35

Exercise 2b
1 (a) 3, -1, 3, -2, 3 Ans 7 **(b) (i)** 9 **(ii)** 2 **(iii)** permutations of 3 correct, 4 incorrect, 3 not attempted
2 (a) 72° (±2°) **(b) (i)** 53° **(ii)** 62° **(iii)** 56°
3 (a) (i) 64 **(ii)** 7 **(iii)** 125 **(b)** 0.625
4 (a) (i) 5 **(ii)** 32 **(iii)** 3 **(b)** 6x + 15
5 (a) (i) $\frac{3}{8}$ **(ii)** $\frac{1}{3}$ **(b)** 8°C
6 (a) (i) £2.63 **(ii)** £2.37 **(b) (i)** 3 **(ii)** +6 , −6

Exercise 3b

1 (a) Enniskillen and Larne **(b)** Downpatrick and Portrush **(c)** 100 miles
2 (a) (i) 279 **(ii)** 7 thousand **(b) (i)** 81 **(ii)** 8
3 (a) 4 **(b)** −3 , −7 **(c)** −5x − 10
4 (a) (i) $\frac{11}{12}$ **(ii)** $\frac{13}{20}$ or 0.65 **(b)** 20%
5 (a) 10a − 3b **(b)** 8
6 (a) (i) 6.28 **(ii)** 0.29 **(b) (i)** £1.52 **(ii)** £3.48 **(c)** 0.07
7 (a) 3a + 2b **(b)** x^2 − 3x

Exercise 4b

1 (2, -1) and (-3, 0) plotted accurately
2 (a) 240 cm³ **(b)** 3 cm
3 (a) 47 and 79 **(b)** 81
4 net drawn
5 (a) (i) 69° **(ii)** 111° **(b)** 63°
6 Bar chart accurately drawn with axes labelled

Exercise 1c

1 (a) £2.10 + £ 3.15 + £0.41 = £5.66 **(b)** £4.34 **(c)** 5
2 (a) 26.52cm² **(b)** 22.4 cm
3 (a) (i) 1.5 **(ii)** 10.89 **(b)** 4.91 **(c)** £30
4 (a) £28.50 **(b)** 5 days
5 (a) £2.02 **(b)** £420
6 (a) (i) 6023 **(ii)** £3011.50 **(b)** 7200 **(c)** 400

Exercise 2c

1 Pie chart angles corresponding to order in which the types are listed 72°, 126°, 90°, 18°, 54°
2 £486
3 (a) 11 **(b)** 65p
4 (a) $\frac{5}{8}$ **(b)** 90% **(c)** $\frac{11}{20}$
5 (a) 130.09 **(b) (i)** 2363 units **(ii)** £260.40 **(c) (i)** £8.00 **(ii)** £168.00
6 (a) £283.32 **(b)** £233.05

CHEMISTRY 3(ii) — ENERGY AND CHEMICAL TESTS

PHYSICS 3(i) — FORCES AND WAVES

PHYSICS 3(ii) — MAGNETISM AND STARS

EXAM SKILLS

Published by Coordination Group Publications Ltd.

From original material by Richard Parsons.

Editors:
Ellen Bowness, Gemma Hallam, Sarah Hilton, Sharon Keeley, Andy Park, Alan Rix, David Ryan, Julie Wakeling.

Contributors:
Mike Bossart, Jason Howell, Adrian Schmit, Mike Thompson.

Graph to show trend in atmospheric CO_2 concentration and global temperature on page 1 based on data by EPICA Community Members 2004 and Siegenthaler et al 2005.

ISBN: 978 1 84762 326 3

Groovy website: www.cgpbooks.co.uk

Printed by Elanders Ltd, Newcastle upon Tyne.
Jolly bits of clipart from CorelDRAW®

Introducing How Science Works

Science isn't just a long, unchanging list of facts. It's <u>growing</u> and <u>evolving</u> all the time, as scientists develop <u>new theories</u> and <u>gather evidence</u> to test them. Global warming is a good example...

Taking the Temperature of a Planet Is Hard

Years ago, a French scientist worked out that <u>atmospheric gases</u>, including CO_2, keep the Earth at a <u>temperature</u> that's <u>just right</u>. Later, a Swedish chemist, Arrhenius, predicted that as people <u>burnt more coal</u>, the <u>concentration of CO_2</u> in the atmosphere would <u>rise</u>, and the <u>Earth would get warmer</u>.

1) To <u>test</u> this <u>hypothesis</u>, you need <u>reliable data</u> for <u>two variables</u> — the <u>CO_2 level</u> and <u>temperature</u>. To be <u>valid</u>, the investigation has to cover the <u>whole globe</u> over <u>hundreds of thousands of years</u> (or we'd just discover that it was colder during the last <u>ice age</u>, which we know anyway).

2) To monitor <u>global temperature</u>, scientists often measure the temperature of the <u>sea surface</u>.

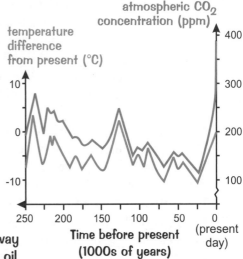

The first measurements were done from ships — some bloke would fling a <u>bucket</u> overboard, haul it up and stick a <u>thermometer</u> in it. Later, ships recorded the temperature of the water they took on board to cool their engines. Neither method was exactly great —
- Water samples weren't all taken from the same <u>depth</u> (and deeper water is usually <u>colder</u>).
- The sailors taking the readings were probably a bit <u>slapdash</u> — they were busy <u>sailing</u>.
  So if two samples were taken in the same place, at the same time, the results would quite possibly be different — in other words, not <u>reproducible</u>.
- Ships didn't go <u>everywhere</u>, so the records are a bit <u>patchy</u>. So, you might see that the North Atlantic ocean is getting warmer, but have no idea about the rest of the world. The original hypothesis was about <u>global</u> temperature, so the <u>validity</u> of these results is <u>doubtful</u>.

3) Today, things are much better — we can measure sea surface temperature from <u>satellites</u>, with modern, <u>accurate</u> instruments. These results are <u>reliable</u>, and they give us <u>global coverage</u>.

4) We also have very <u>clever</u> ways of finding temperatures and CO_2 levels from the <u>distant past</u> (before thermometers existed) — by examining <u>air bubbles</u> trapped deep in the <u>ice</u> in <u>Antarctica</u>, for example. There are similar tricks involving <u>tree rings</u>, <u>sediments</u> and pollen, so the results can be checked. Even so, these methods <u>aren't perfect</u> — there may be contamination problems, for instance.

Interpreting the Data Is Even Harder...

1) This is a graph of the <u>CO_2</u> and <u>global temperature</u> data. It shows temperature and CO_2 rising very rapidly from about 1850 (when the <u>Industrial Revolution</u> began).

2) <u>But</u> the graph also shows that there have been <u>huge changes</u> in the climate before — you could argue that the recent warming is just part of that <u>natural variability</u>.

3) There's a <u>scientific consensus</u> that the warming is <u>more</u> than natural variation and that <u>humans</u> are <u>causing</u> it — we're emitting too much CO_2. If that's right, maybe we should <u>stop burning fossil fuels</u>.

4) But there are big <u>interests</u> at stake, and this can influence the way people <u>present</u> the data. If we stopped buying fossil fuels then oil companies, among others, would lose out — so they might emphasise the 'natural variation' argument. People with different interests (like wind turbine manufacturers) might emphasise the more recent rapid rise in temperature and CO_2. They could use exactly the <u>same data</u> — but with a <u>different slant</u>.

atmospheric CO_2 concentration (ppm)

temperature difference from present (°C)

Time before present (1000s of years)

(present day)

How science works — slowly and painfully...

So, here's how it works — you: 1) observe something (Earth's warming up); 2) come up with a theory to explain it (increasing greenhouse effect); 3) gather <u>valid</u>, <u>reliable evidence</u> to test your theory. If the evidence <u>doesn't</u> match what you predicted, you need to <u>tweak your theory and retest</u>, or <u>start again</u>...

Gas and Solute Exchange

The processes that keep organisms alive won't happen without the right raw materials.
And the raw materials have to get to the right places. It's like making chicken soup.
You need the chicken in your kitchen. It's no good if it's still at the supermarket.

Substances Move by Diffusion, Osmosis and Active Transport

1) Life processes need <u>gases or other dissolved substances</u> before they can happen.

2) For example, for <u>photosynthesis</u> to happen, carbon dioxide and water have to get into plant cells. And for <u>respiration</u> to take place, glucose and oxygen both have to get inside cells.

3) <u>Waste substances</u> also need to move out of the cells so that the organism can get rid of them.

4) These substances move to where they need to be by <u>diffusion</u>, <u>osmosis</u> and <u>active transport</u>.

5) <u>Diffusion</u> is where particles move from an area of <u>high concentration</u> to an area of <u>low concentration</u>. For example, different gases can simply diffuse through one another, like when a weird smell spreads out through a room. Alternatively, dissolved particles can diffuse in and out of cells through <u>cell membranes</u>.

6) <u>Osmosis</u> is similar, but it only refers to <u>water</u>. The water moves across a <u>partially permeable membrane</u> (e.g. a cell membrane) from an area of <u>high water concentration</u> to an area of <u>low water concentration</u> — see your Biology 2 notes for more about diffusion and osmosis.

7) Diffusion and osmosis both involve stuff moving from an area where there's a <u>high concentration</u> of it, to an area where there's a <u>lower concentration</u> of it. Sometimes substances need to move in the <u>other direction</u> — which is where <u>active transport</u> comes in — see page 5.

8) In life processes, the gases and dissolved substances have to move through some sort of <u>exchange surface</u>. The exchange surface structures have to allow <u>enough</u> of the necessary substances to pass through.

Exchange surfaces are ADAPTED to maximise effectiveness.

The Structure of Leaves Lets Gases Diffuse In and Out of Cells

1) Carbon dioxide <u>diffuses into the air spaces</u> within the leaf, then it <u>diffuses into the cells</u> where photosynthesis happens. The leaf's structure is <u>adapted</u> so that this can happen easily.

2) The underneath of the leaf is an <u>exchange surface</u>. It's covered in tiny little holes called <u>stomata</u> which the carbon dioxide diffuses in through.

3) <u>Water vapour</u> and <u>oxygen</u> also diffuse <u>out</u> through the stomata. (Water vapour is actually lost from all over the leaf surface, but most of it is lost through the stomata.)

4) The size of the stomata are controlled by <u>guard cells</u>. These <u>close</u> the stomata if the plant is losing water faster than it is being replaced by the roots. Without these guard cells the plant would soon <u>wilt</u>.

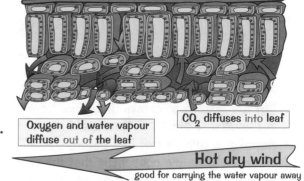

Oxygen and water vapour diffuse out of the leaf

CO_2 diffuses into leaf

Hot dry wind
good for carrying the water vapour away

5) The <u>flattened shape</u> of the leaf increases the <u>area</u> of this exchange surface so that it's more effective.

6) The <u>walls of the cells</u> inside the leaf form another exchange surface. The <u>air spaces</u> inside the leaf increase the <u>area</u> of this surface so there's more chance for carbon dioxide to get into the cells.

> The water vapour escapes by diffusion because there's a lot of it <u>inside</u> the leaf and less of it in the <u>air outside</u>. This diffusion is called <u>transpiration</u> and it goes <u>quicker</u> when the air around the leaf is kept <u>dry</u> — i.e. transpiration is quickest in <u>hot</u>, <u>dry</u>, <u>windy conditions</u> — and don't you forget it!

I say stomaaarta, you say stomaaayta...

The cells on the <u>stem</u> of a <u>cactus</u> photosynthesise and have <u>stomata-like holes</u> to let gases in. The cacti don't want to lose much water, so the holes only open at <u>night</u> when it's <u>cooler</u>. The cacti are adapted so that they can <u>store</u> the CO_2 that diffuses in at night until <u>daylight</u> when it's used for photosynthesis.

The Breathing System

You need to get <u>oxygen</u> from the air into your bloodstream so that it can get to your cells for <u>respiration</u>. You also need to get rid of <u>carbon dioxide</u> in your blood. This all happens inside the <u>lungs</u>. Breathing is how the air gets <u>in and out</u> of your <u>lungs</u>. Breathing's definitely a useful skill to have. You'll need to be able to do it to get through the exam.

The Lungs Are in the Thorax

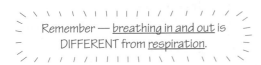

1) The <u>thorax</u> is the top part of your 'body'.
2) It's separated from the lower part of the body by the <u>diaphragm</u>.
3) The lungs are like big pink <u>sponges</u> and are protected by the <u>ribcage</u>.
4) The air that you breathe in goes through the <u>trachea</u>. This splits into two tubes called '<u>bronchi</u>' (each one is 'a bronchus'), one going to each lung.
5) The bronchi split into progressively smaller tubes called <u>bronchioles</u>.
6) The bronchioles finally end at small bags called <u>alveoli</u> where the gas exchange takes place.

Remember — <u>breathing in and out</u> is DIFFERENT from <u>respiration</u>.

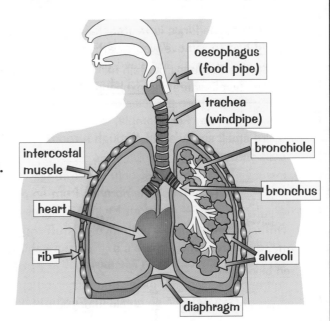

Breathing In...

1) <u>Intercostal muscles</u> and <u>diaphragm contract</u>.
2) Thorax volume <u>increases</u>.
3) This decreases the pressure, drawing air <u>in</u>.

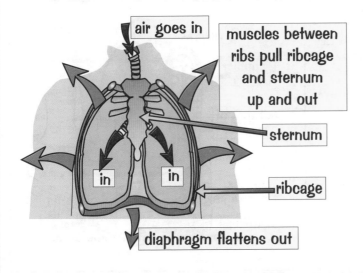

...and Breathing Out

1) <u>Intercostal muscles</u> and <u>diaphragm relax</u>.
2) Thorax volume <u>decreases</u>.
3) Air is forced <u>out</u>.

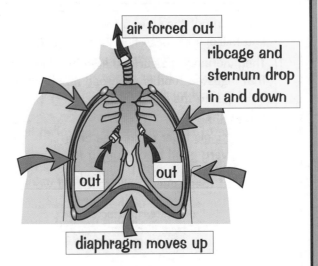

Stop huffing and puffing and just LEARN IT...

So when you breathe in, you don't have to suck the air in. You just make the space in your lungs <u>bigger</u> and the air rushes in to fill it. The small bags called <u>alveoli</u> at the ends of the air passages are the really interesting bit. It's through the alveoli that the <u>oxygen</u> gets into the blood supply to be carted off round the body. Also, the waste <u>carbon dioxide</u> gets out of the blood supply here so it can be breathed out. This is all explained on the next page, so once you've got this one learned, flip over and off you trot.

Diffusion Through Cell Membranes

This page is about how two different parts of the human body are adapted so that substances can diffuse through them most effectively. The first bit is about how gases in the lungs get into and out of the blood. The second is about how digested food gets from the gut to the blood.

Gas Exchange Happens in the Lungs

The job of the lungs is to transfer oxygen to the blood and to remove waste carbon dioxide from it.

To do this the lungs contain millions of little air sacs called alveoli where gas exchange takes place.

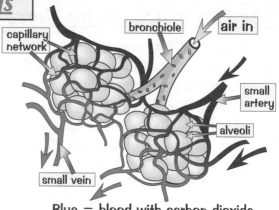

Blue = blood with carbon dioxide.
Red = blood with oxygen.

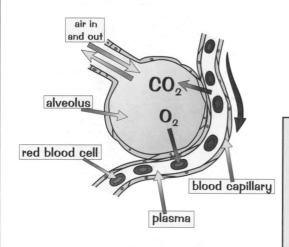

The alveoli are specialised to maximise the diffusion of oxygen and CO_2. They have:

- An enormous surface area (about 75m² in humans).
- A moist lining for dissolving gases.
- Very thin walls.
- A copious blood supply.

The Villi Provide a Really Really Big Surface Area

The inside of the small intestine is covered in millions and millions of these tiny little projections called villi.

They increase the surface area in a big way so that digested food is absorbed much more quickly into the blood.

Notice they have
- a single layer of surface cells
- a very good blood supply to assist quick absorption.

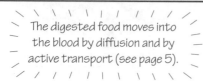

The digested food moves into the blood by diffusion and by active transport (see page 5).

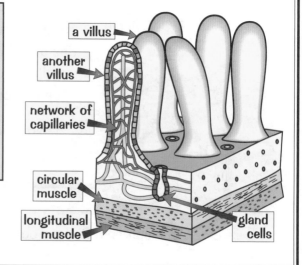

Al Veoli — the Italian gas man...

Living organisms are really well adapted for getting the substances they need to their cells. It makes sense — if they couldn't do this well, they'd die out. A large surface area is a key way that organisms' exchange surfaces are made more effective — molecules can only diffuse through a membrane when they're right next to it, and a large surface area means loads more molecules are close to the membrane. If you're asked how something's adapted for a job, think about if surface area is important.

Active Transport

Sometimes substances need to be absorbed against a concentration gradient, i.e. from a lower to a higher concentration. This process is lovingly referred to as ACTIVE TRANSPORT.

Root Hairs are Specialised for Absorbing Water and Minerals

Root Hair cell

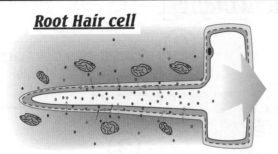

1) The cells on the surface of plant roots grow into long "hairs" which stick out into the soil.

2) This gives the plant a big surface area for absorbing water and mineral ions from the soil.

3) Most of the water and mineral ions that get into a plant are absorbed by the root hair cells.

Root Hairs Take in Minerals Using Active Transport

1) The concentration of minerals is usually higher in the root hair cell than in the soil around it.

2) So normal diffusion doesn't explain how minerals are taken up into the root hair cell.

3) They should go the other way if they followed the rules of diffusion.

4) The answer is that a conveniently mysterious process called "active transport" is responsible.

5) Active transport allows the plant to absorb minerals against a concentration gradient. This is essential for its growth. But active transport needs ENERGY from respiration to make it work.

6) Active transport also happens in humans, for example in taking glucose from the gut (see below), and from the kidney tubules.

We Need Active Transport to Stop Us Starving

Active transport is used in the gut when there is a low concentration of nutrients in the gut, but a high concentration of nutrients in the blood.

1) When there's a higher concentration of glucose and amino acids in the gut they diffuse naturally into the blood.

2) BUT — sometimes there's a lower concentration of nutrients in the gut than there is in the blood.

3) This means that the concentration gradient is the wrong way.

4) The same process used in plant roots is used here....
   ..."Active transport".

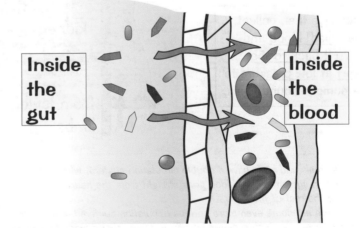

Inside the gut

Inside the blood

5) Active transport allows nutrients to be taken into the blood, despite the fact that the concentration gradient is the wrong way.

Active transport sucks...

An important difference between active transport and diffusion is that active transport uses energy. Imagine a pen of sheep in a field. If you open the pen, the sheep will happily diffuse from the area of high sheep concentration into the field, which has a low sheep concentration — you won't have to do a thing. To get them back in the pen though, you'll have to put in quite a bit of energy.

The Circulation System

The circulation system's main function is to get <u>food and oxygen</u> to every cell in the body. As well as being a delivery service, it's also a waste collection service — it carries <u>waste products</u> like <u>carbon dioxide</u> and <u>urea</u> to where they can be removed from the body.

The <u>DOUBLE</u> Circulation System, *Actually*

The <u>heart</u> is actually <u>two pumps</u>. The <u>right side</u> pumps deoxygenated blood to the <u>lungs</u> to <u>collect oxygen</u> and <u>remove carbon dioxide</u>.
Then the <u>left side</u> pumps this oxygenated blood <u>around the body</u>.

①

② <u>Arteries</u> carry blood <u>away from the heart</u> at <u>high pressure</u>.

③ Normally, arteries carry <u>oxygenated blood</u> and veins carry <u>deoxygenated blood</u>.

The <u>pulmonary artery</u> and <u>pulmonary vein</u> are the <u>big exceptions</u> to this rule (see diagram).

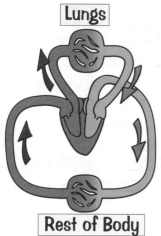

Lungs

Rest of Body

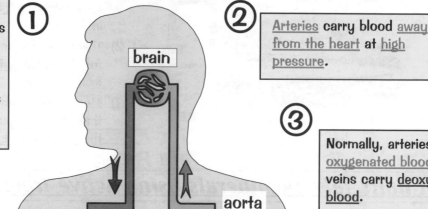

brain

lungs

aorta

pulmonary artery

pulmonary vein

vena cava

heart

liver

gut

kidneys

from lower limbs

to lower limbs

④ The arteries eventually split off into thousands of tiny <u>capillaries</u> which take blood to <u>every cell</u> in the body.

⑤ The <u>veins</u> then collect the <u>"used"</u> blood and carry it <u>back to the heart</u> at <u>low pressure</u> to be pumped round again.

All mammals and birds have a double circulation system, while fish only have a single circulation system — the blood goes straight from the heart to the gills (their lungs), then to the rest of the body.
And there are some even more curious circulation systems, e.g. worms have five pairs of hearts, (which seems a bit silly to me as that's nine more that can be broken), and flat worms don't actually have any circulation system. It's all very odd. But then life's full of little mysteries isn't it!

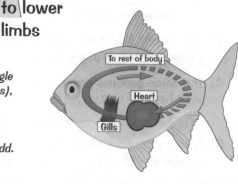

To rest of body

Heart

Gills

<u>Blood vessels — a vampire's favourite type of ship...</u>

The diagram above only shows the <u>basic layout</u>. There's actually <u>zillions</u> of blood vessels. If you laid all your arteries, capillaries and veins end to end, they'd go around the world about three times. These vessels vary from hose-pipe width <u>arteries</u> to <u>capillaries</u> that are a tenth of the thickness of a human hair.

Blood

This stuff's the nitty gritty about blood. Make sure you learn it all.

Capillaries Deliver Food and Oxygen to Each Cell

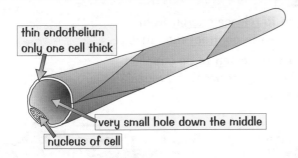

thin endothelium
only one cell thick

very small hole down the middle

nucleus of cell

1) Capillaries use diffusion to deliver <u>food</u> and <u>oxygen</u> direct to body tissues and take <u>carbon dioxide</u> and other <u>waste materials</u> away.

2) Their walls are usually only <u>one cell thick</u> to make it easy for stuff to pass in and out of them.

3) They are <u>too small</u> to see without a microscope.

Blood is Made Up of Four Main Parts

Blood consists of:
- <u>white blood cells</u> (see your Biology 1a notes for more details)
- <u>red blood cells</u> (see below)
- <u>plasma</u> (see below)
- <u>platelets</u> — these are small fragments of cells that help blood to clot at a wound.

Red Blood Cells Carry Oxygen

1) The job of red blood cells is to carry <u>oxygen</u> from the lungs to all the cells in the body.

2) They have a doughnut shape to give a <u>large surface area</u> for absorbing <u>oxygen</u>.

3) They <u>don't</u> have a nucleus — this allows more room to carry oxygen.

4) They contain a substance called <u>haemoglobin</u>.

5) In the <u>lungs</u>, haemoglobin combines with <u>oxygen</u> to become <u>oxyhaemoglobin</u>. In body tissues the reverse happens to release oxygen to the <u>cells</u>.

The more red blood cells you've got, the more oxygen can get to your cells. At high altitudes there's less oxygen in the air — so people who live there produce more red blood cells to compensate.

Plasma is the Liquid That Carries Everything in Blood

This is a pale straw-coloured liquid which <u>carries just about everything</u>:

1) <u>Red</u> and <u>white blood cells</u> and <u>platelets</u>.

2) Nutrients like <u>glucose</u> and <u>amino acids</u>. These are the soluble products of digestion which are absorbed from the gut and taken to the cells of the body.

3) <u>Carbon dioxide</u> from the organs to the lungs.

4) <u>Urea</u> from the liver to the kidneys.

5) <u>Hormones</u>.

6) <u>Antibodies</u> and <u>antitoxins</u> produced by the white blood cells.

Advice for a vampire — drink your soup before it clots...

Red blood cells are <u>perfectly designed</u> for absorbing plenty of oxygen and squeezing through capillaries. There's a condition called <u>sickle-cell anaemia</u> in which the red blood cells are <u>crescent-moon shapes</u>. This causes problems because <u>less oxygen</u> is carried and the cells <u>don't flow well</u> through the capillaries.

Exercise

When you exercise, your body quickly adapts so that your muscles get <u>more oxygen and glucose</u> to supply <u>energy</u>. If your body can't get enough oxygen or glucose to them, it has some back-up plans ready.

Exercise *Increases the* Heart Rate

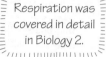

Respiration was covered in detail in Biology 2.

1) Muscles are made of <u>muscle cells</u>. These use <u>oxygen</u> to <u>release energy</u> from <u>glucose</u> (this process is called <u>respiration</u>), which is used to <u>contract</u> the muscles.

2) An <u>increase</u> in muscle activity requires <u>more glucose and oxygen</u> to be supplied to the muscle cells. Extra carbon dioxide needs to be <u>removed</u> from the muscle cells. For this to happen the blood has to flow at a <u>faster</u> rate.

3) This is why physical activity:

- <u>increases</u> your <u>breathing rate</u> and makes you breathe <u>more deeply</u> to meet the demand for <u>extra oxygen</u>.
- <u>increases</u> the speed at which the <u>heart pumps</u>.
- <u>dilates</u> (makes wider) the <u>arteries</u> which supply blood to the muscles.

Glycogen *is Used During Exercise*

1) Some <u>glucose</u> from food is <u>stored</u> as <u>glycogen</u>.

2) Glycogen's mainly stored in the liver, but each <u>muscle</u> also has its own store.

3) During vigorous exercise, muscles use glucose <u>rapidly</u>, and have to draw on their <u>glycogen stores</u> to provide more energy. If the exercise goes on for a while the glycogen stores get <u>used up</u>.

4) When the glycogen stores <u>run low</u>, the muscles <u>don't</u> get the energy they need to keep contracting, and they <u>get tired</u>.

Anaerobic Respiration *is Used if There's* Not Enough Oxygen

1) When you do vigorous exercise and your body can't supply enough <u>oxygen</u> to your muscles, they start doing <u>anaerobic respiration</u> instead of aerobic respiration.

2) "Anaerobic" just means "<u>without</u> oxygen". It's the <u>incomplete</u> breakdown of glucose, which produces <u>lactic acid</u>.

glucose → energy + lactic acid

3) This is <u>NOT the best way to convert glucose into energy</u> because <u>lactic acid</u> builds up in the muscles, which gets <u>painful</u>. This also causes the muscles to get <u>tired</u>.

4) Another downside is that <u>anaerobic respiration</u> does <u>not release nearly as much energy</u> as aerobic respiration — but it's useful in emergencies.

5) The <u>advantage</u> is that at least you can keep on using your muscles for a while longer.

Anaerobic Respiration Leads to an Oxygen Debt

1) After resorting to anaerobic respiration, when you stop exercising you'll have an "<u>oxygen debt</u>".

2) In other words you have to "<u>repay</u>" the oxygen that you didn't get to your muscles in time, because your <u>lungs</u>, <u>heart</u> and <u>blood</u> couldn't keep up with the <u>demand</u> earlier on.

3) This means you have to keep breathing hard for a while <u>after you stop</u>, to get oxygen into your muscles to oxidise the painful lactic acid to harmless CO_2 and water.

4) While <u>high levels</u> of <u>CO_2</u> and <u>lactic acid</u> are detected in the blood (by the brain), the <u>pulse</u> and <u>breathing rate</u> stay high to try and rectify the situation.

Too much keep-fit makes your head spin round — like in the Exorcist...

Phew... I bet you're exhausted after reading this page. Yeast also respire <u>anaerobically</u>, but they produce <u>ethanol</u> (and carbon dioxide) — see page 13. It's a good job that humans produce <u>lactic acid</u> instead — or after a bit of vigorous exercise we'd all be staggering around drunk.

Kidneys

The kidneys are really important organs. They get rid of toxic waste like urea as well as adjusting the amount of dissolved ions and water in the blood. The kidneys were introduced in the Biology 2 Unit, but here's the rest of the stuff you need to know.

Nephrons Are the Filtration Units in the Kidneys

1) Ultrafiltration:

1) A high pressure is built up which squeezes water, urea, ions and sugar out of the blood and into the Bowman's capsule.

2) The membranes between the blood vessels and the Bowman's capsule act like filters, so big molecules like proteins and blood cells are not squeezed out. They stay in the blood.

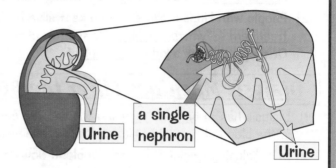

a single nephron

Urine

Urine

Enlarged View of a Single Nephron

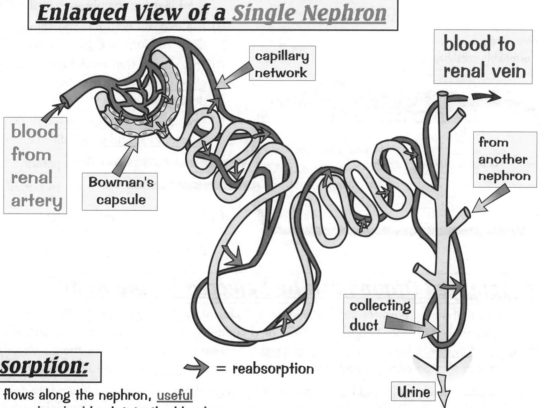

capillary network

blood to renal vein

blood from renal artery

Bowman's capsule

from another nephron

collecting duct

⟹ = reabsorption

Urine

2) Reabsorption:

As the liquid flows along the nephron, useful substances are reabsorbed back into the blood:

1) All the sugar is reabsorbed. This involves the process of active transport against the concentration gradient.

2) Sufficient ions are reabsorbed. Excess ions are not. Active transport is needed.

3) Sufficient water is reabsorbed.

3) Release of wastes:

The remaining substances (including urea) continue out of the nephron, into the ureter and down to the bladder as urine.

Don't try to kid-me that you know it all — learn it properly...

The kidneys are pretty complicated organs as you can see. Luckily you don't have to learn all the ins and outs of the diagram — but you do have to make sure you know exactly what happens in each of the three stages. Learn what's filtered, what's reabsorbed and what's released as urine.

Kidney Failure

If someone's kidneys stop working, there are basically two treatments — regular dialysis or a transplant.

The Kidneys Remove Waste Substances from the Blood

1) If the kidneys don't work properly, waste substances build up in the blood and you lose your ability to control the levels of ions and water in your body. Eventually, this results in death.

2) People with kidney failure can be kept alive by having dialysis treatment — where machines do the job of the kidneys. Or they can have a kidney transplant.

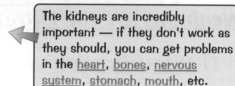

The kidneys are incredibly important — if they don't work as they should, you can get problems in the heart, bones, nervous system, stomach, mouth, etc.

Dialysis Machines Filter the Blood

1) Dialysis has to be done regularly to keep the concentrations of dissolved substances in the blood at normal levels, and to remove waste substances.

2) In a dialysis machine the person's blood flows alongside a selectively permeable barrier, surrounded by dialysis fluid. It's permeable to things like ions and waste substances, but not big molecules like proteins (just like the membranes in the kidney).

dialysis fluid out

selectively permeable membrane

dialysis fluid in

Waste products diffuse out into dialysis fluid

from person

back to person

3) The dialysis fluid has the same concentration of dissolved ions and glucose as healthy blood.

4) This means that useful dissolved ions and glucose won't be lost from the blood during dialysis.

5) Only waste substances (such as urea) and excess ions and water diffuse across the barrier.

6) Many patients with kidney failure have to have a dialysis session three times a week. Each session takes 3-4 hours — not much fun.

Transplanted Organs can be Rejected by the Body

At the moment, the only cure for kidney disease is to have a kidney transplant. Healthy kidneys are usually transplanted from people who have died suddenly, say in a car accident, and who are on the organ donor register or carry a donor card (provided their relatives give the go-ahead). But kidneys can also be transplanted from people who are still alive — as we all have two of them.

The donor kidney can be rejected by the patient's immune system — treated like a foreign body and attacked by antibodies. To help prevent this happening, precautions are taken:

1) A donor with a tissue type that closely matches the patient is chosen. Tissue type is based on the antigens that are on the surface of most cells. *(You covered antigens in Biology 1a.)*

2) The patient's bone marrow is zapped with radiation to stop white blood cells being produced — so they won't attack the transplanted kidney. They also have to take drugs that suppress the immune system.

3) Unfortunately, this means that the patient can't fight any disease that comes along, so they have to be kept in totally sterile conditions for some time after the operation.

Dialysis or transplant? Both have their downsides...

Kidney dialysis machines are expensive things for the NHS to run — and dialysis is not a pleasant experience. Transplants can put an end to the hours spent on dialysis, but there are long waiting lists for kidneys. Even if one with a matching tissue type is found, there's the possibility that it'll be rejected. And taking drugs that suppress the immune system means the person is vulnerable to other illnesses.

Revision Summary for Biology 3(i)

It's no good just reading the section through and hoping you've got it all — it'll only stick if you've learned it <u>properly</u>. These questions are designed to really test whether you know all your stuff — ignore them at your peril. OK, rant over — I'll leave it to you...

1) What's the name for the process that's happening when water moves across a partially permeable membrane to equalise the concentrations on either side?

2) Explain how leaves are adapted to maximise the amount of carbon dioxide that gets to their cells.

3) Why do the leaves care if carbon dioxide gets to their cells or not?

4) What are the pores in the leaves called?

5) Name the main substances that diffuse out of leaves.

6) What conditions does transpiration happen most quickly in?

7) Cacti, which grow in the desert, have spikes instead of flat leaves. Why is this?

8) Name the chest cavity that's above the diaphragm.

9) Describe the gas exchange that happens between the alveoli and the blood.

10) Give four ways that the alveoli's structure is ideal for gas exchange.

11) How does the structure of a villus make it good at its job?

12) Give the two main differences between active transport and diffusion.

13) Why can't most mineral ions get into roots by diffusion?

14) Draw a diagram of a root hair cell. Why is it this shape?

15) Does glucose <u>only</u> get into the blood from the gut by active transport?

16) Explain why our circulation system is called a *double* circulation system.

17) Describe the pressure and oxygen content of the blood in veins and arteries.
    What are the big words for saying if the blood has oxygen in or not?

18) Sketch a red blood cell. Why is it this shape?

19) What's the substance in red blood cells called? What is it called when it combines with oxygen?

20)* Some companies sell special tents for athletes to sleep in. These tents have a lower oxygen concentration than the air at sea level has.

    a) Explain why an athlete might buy one of these tents.

    b) How could an athlete achieve the same effect without buying one of these tents?

21) Why does your heart beat faster when you do exercise?

22)* The table below shows the oxygen consumption of an athlete as her heart beats at different rates.

Heart rate (BPM)	85	105	118	125	143	148	152	163
Oxygen consumption (ml/kg/min)	13	26	30	33	40	47	53	56

    a) Draw a scattergraph of the data and a line of best fit.

    b) What does this graph show?

    c) Explain why this relationship exists.

23) What is "anaerobic respiration"? Give the word equation for what happens in our bodies.

24) Give two reasons why anaerobic respiration isn't the best way to release energy.

25) Explain how you repay an oxygen debt.

26) Name three things that are reabsorbed by kidneys.

27) Explain why sugar doesn't simply <u>diffuse</u> back into the blood from the nephrons.

28) How does kidney dialysis work?.

29) What are the advantages and disadvantages of a kidney transplant over dialysis?

30) Why do transplant patients have their immune systems suppressed?

* Answers on page 76

Biology 3(i) — Life Processes

Food and Drink from Microorganisms

Microorganisms, such as bacteria, cause changes in food — often the changes are <u>bad</u>, but sometimes they're <u>useful</u> and mean we can have foods that we wouldn't have otherwise.

The Theory of Biogenesis Has Been Developed Over the Years

1) People used to think that life could <u>spontaneously generate</u> (just appear) from <u>non-living</u> material.

2) But then <u>evidence</u> showed that this <u>couldn't</u> be the case. The evidence supported the theory that living things are created from <u>other living organisms</u> — this is the theory of <u>biogenesis</u>.

3) Here's how the accepted theory was <u>changed</u> to fit the available evidence:

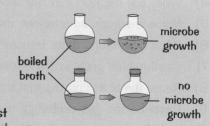

Before 1765 it was believed that <u>substances in food</u> were changed into <u>microbes</u>, which caused the food to go off.

A scientist called <u>Lazzaro Spallanzani</u> <u>boiled</u> two sets of broth to <u>kill the microbes</u>, then <u>sealed</u> one flask and left the other <u>open</u>. Only the <u>open</u> one went off (although the broth in the sealed flask did go off when it was left open later).

This showed that <u>microbes</u> got into the food from the <u>air</u>, but opponents just thought that it meant <u>air</u> from outside the flask was necessary to <u>start the change</u>.

The theory that 'fresh' air caused substances in food to change into microbes was <u>disproved</u> by <u>Theodor Schwann</u> in 1837. He showed that meat would <u>not</u> go off in air, provided the air was <u>heated</u> first to <u>kill microorganisms</u>.

A <u>more conclusive experiment</u> was carried out by the famous scientist <u>Louis Pasteur</u> in 1859.

He heated broth in two flasks, <u>both</u> of which were left <u>open</u> to the air. However, one of the flasks had a <u>curved neck</u> so that bacteria in the air would settle in the loop, and <u>not get through</u> to the broth.

The broth in the flask with the <u>curved neck</u> stayed <u>fresh</u>, proving that it was the <u>microbes</u> and not the air causing it to go off.

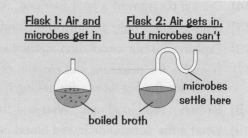

Most Cheese is Made Using Bacteria...

Yummy. Here's what happens:

1) A culture of <u>bacteria</u> is added to <u>milk</u>.
2) The bacteria produce solid <u>curds</u> in the milk.
3) The curds are <u>separated</u> from the liquid whey.
4) <u>More bacteria</u> are sometimes added to the curds, and the whole lot is left to <u>ripen</u> for a while.
5) <u>Moulds</u> are added to give <u>blue cheese</u> (e.g. Stilton) its colour and taste.

Yoghurt is Made Using Bacteria Too

<u>Bacteria</u> are used to <u>clot milk</u> during the manufacture of <u>yoghurt</u>.

1) The milk is often <u>heat treated</u> first to <u>kill off any bacteria</u> that may be in it, then cooled.
2) A <u>starter culture</u> of bacteria is then added. The bacteria ferment the <u>lactose sugar</u> (present in the milk) to <u>lactic acid</u>.
3) The acid causes the milk to <u>clot</u> and solidify into <u>yoghurt</u>.
4) Sterilised flavours (e.g. <u>fruit</u>) are sometimes then added.

So bacteria aren't always the bad guys...

It seems weird. Microorganisms in food can make you <u>ill</u> — that's why you should <u>wash your hands</u> before touching food and the reason you have to make sure meat is <u>cooked thoroughly</u>. Yet some foods are <u>made with microorganisms</u>, and as you'll see on page 14, some food <u>is</u> microorganisms.

Using Yeast

There's nothing newfangled about yeast. It's been used for donkey's years to make bread and alcohol.

Yeast *is a Single-Celled Fungus*

Yeast is a <u>microorganism</u>. A yeast cell has a <u>nucleus</u>, <u>cytoplasm</u>, a <u>vacuole</u>, and a <u>cell membrane</u> surrounded by a <u>cell wall</u>.

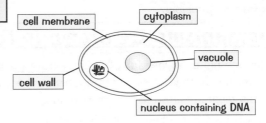

Yeast *Can Respire With or Without Oxygen*

Learn the <u>equation for anaerobic respiration</u> (i.e. without oxygen) of glucose by yeast (this process is called <u>fermentation</u>):

> glucose → ethanol + carbon dioxide + energy

Yeast can also respire <u>aerobically</u> (i.e. with oxygen). This produces much <u>more energy</u>, and is needed to <u>grow</u> and <u>reproduce</u>:

> glucose + oxygen → carbon dioxide + water + energy

This is the same respiration process that releases energy in animals and plants.

Yeast *is Used to Make Bread*

Holes in the bread, which make it nice and light, are made by carbon dioxide bubbles in the dough.

1) Yeast is used in <u>dough</u> to produce nice, light bread.
2) The yeast converts sugars to <u>carbon dioxide</u> and some <u>ethanol</u>. It is the <u>carbon dioxide</u> that makes the bread <u>rise</u>.
3) As the carbon dioxide <u>expands</u>, it gets trapped in the dough, making it lighter.

Yeast *is Used to Make Alcoholic Drinks*

Here's how beer is brewed:

1) Beer is made from <u>grain</u> — usually <u>barley</u>.
2) The barley grains are allowed to <u>germinate</u> for a few days, during which the <u>starch</u> in the grains is broken down into <u>sugar</u> by <u>enzymes</u>. Then the grains are <u>dried</u> in a kiln. This process is called <u>malting</u>.
3) The malted grain is <u>mashed up</u> and water is added to produce a <u>sugary solution</u> with lots of bits in it. This is then sieved to remove the bits.
4) <u>Hops</u> are added to the mixture to give the beer its <u>bitter flavour</u>.
5) The sugary solution is then <u>fermented</u> by <u>yeast</u>, turning the <u>sugar</u> into <u>alcohol</u>.

Germination is when a seed starts to grow into a new plant.

In wine-making, the yeast use the natural sugars in the grape juice as their energy source.

Invite yeast to parties — they're fun guys...

As some fruits get really ripe, the <u>yeast</u> start to ferment the natural sugars and make <u>ethanol</u>. If animals come along and guzzle down lots of the ripened fruit then they'll start to get a bit <u>tipsy</u> — no, seriously, it's true. I'd definitely want to keep out of the way of an elephant that was a bit unsteady on its feet.

Microorganisms in Industry

Shedloads of microorganisms are grown in huge vats called <u>fermenters</u> to make things like <u>antibiotics</u>, <u>fuels</u> and <u>proteins</u>. It's really important to control the conditions in fermenters so that just the stuff you want grows as fast as possible.

Microorganisms _Are Grown in_ Fermenters _on a_ Large Scale

A fermenter is a big container full of <u>liquid culture medium</u> which microorganisms can <u>grow</u> and <u>reproduce</u> in. The fermenter needs to give the microorganisms the <u>conditions</u> they need to <u>grow</u> and produce their <u>useful product</u>. The diagram shows a typical fermenter.

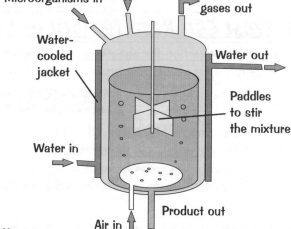

Food in
Microorganisms in
Exhaust gases out
Water-cooled jacket
Water out
Paddles to stir the mixture
Water in
Product out
Air in

1) <u>Food</u> is provided in the liquid culture medium. More can be pumped in if needed.

2) Air is piped in to supply <u>oxygen</u> to the microorganisms.

3) The microorganisms need to be kept at the <u>right temperature</u>. The microorganisms produce <u>heat</u> by respiration, so the fermenters must be <u>cooled</u>. This is usually done with <u>water</u> in a <u>water-cooled jacket</u>. The temperature is monitored by instruments.

4) The <u>right pH</u> is needed for the microorganisms to thrive. Instruments will monitor this.

5) <u>Sterile conditions</u> are needed to <u>prevent contamination</u> from other microorganisms.

6) The microorganisms need to be kept from <u>sinking to the bottom</u>. A <u>motorised stirrer</u> keeps them moving around and maintains an even temperature.

Mycoprotein — _Food from Fermenters_

1) <u>Mycoprotein</u> means <u>protein</u> from <u>fungi</u>. It's a type of <u>single-celled protein</u>.

2) Mycoprotein is used to make <u>meat substitutes</u> for <u>vegetarian</u> meals — Quorn™, for example.

3) A fungus called <u>Fusarium</u> is the main source of mycoprotein.

4) The fungus is grown in <u>fermenters</u>, using <u>glucose syrup</u> as food. The glucose syrup is obtained by <u>digesting maize starch</u> with <u>enzymes</u>.

5) The fungus respires <u>aerobically</u>, so oxygen is supplied, together with nitrogen (as ammonia) and other minerals.

6) It's important to prevent <u>other microorganisms</u> growing in the fermenter. So the fermenter is initially <u>sterilised</u> using steam. The incoming nutrients are <u>heat sterilised</u> and the air supply is <u>filtered</u>.

Penicillin _is Made by Growing_ Mould _in Fermenters_

1) <u>Penicillin</u> is an antibiotic made by growing the <u>mould</u> _Penicillium chrysogenum_ in a fermenter.

2) The mould is grown in a liquid culture medium containing <u>sugar</u> and other nutrients (for example, a source of nitrogen).

3) The sugar is used up as the mould grows.

4) The mould only starts to make penicillin after using up <u>most</u> of the nutrients for <u>growth</u>.

Alexander Fleming discovered Penicillin accidentally in 1928. A culture of bacteria became contaminated with a mould. This mould wiped out areas of bacteria. No one took much notice of Fleming's findings until the Second World War, when the huge number of injuries made it important to find something that would heal infected wounds.

Culture Medium — _sounds very BBC Four to me..._

Food made from microorganisms mightn't sound very appetising, but there are definitely advantages to it. In some <u>developing countries</u> it's difficult to find enough <u>protein</u>. <u>Meat</u> is a big source of protein, but animals need lots of <u>space to graze</u>, plenty of <u>nice grass</u>, etc. <u>Single-celled protein</u> grown in a fermenter is an <u>efficient</u> way of producing protein to feed people. The microorganisms grow <u>very quickly</u>, and don't need much <u>space</u>. And they can even <u>feed</u> on <u>waste material</u> that would be no good for feeding animals.

Fuels from Microorganisms

Food and antibiotics aren't the only things microorganisms can be used for — the stuff they produce can also be used as fuel. And with the world's oil and gas supplies running low, other fuel sources, such as this, are going to become really important.

Fuels Can Be Made by Fermentation

1) Fuels can be made by fermentation of natural products — luckily enough, waste products can often be used.

2) Fermentation is when bacteria or yeast break sugars down by anaerobic respiration.

Anaerobic respiration does not use oxygen.

Ethanol is Made by Anaerobic Fermentation of Sugar

1) Yeast make ethanol when they break down glucose by anaerobic respiration.

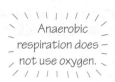

Glucose → Ethanol + Carbon dioxide + Energy

This is the same as the reaction used in wine-making.

2) Sugar cane juices can be used, or glucose can be derived from maize starch by the action of carbohydrase (an enzyme).

3) The ethanol is distilled to separate it from the yeast and remaining glucose before it's used.

4) In some countries, e.g. Brazil, cars are adapted to run on a mixture of ethanol and petrol — this is known as 'gasohol'.

Biogas is Made by Anaerobic Fermentation of Waste Material

1) Biogas is usually about 70% methane (CH_4) and 30% carbon dioxide (CO_2).

2) Lots of different microorganisms are used to produce biogas. They ferment plant and animal waste, which contains carbohydrates. Sludge waste from, e.g. sewage works or sugar factories, is used to make biogas on a large scale.

3) It's made in a simple fermenter called a digester or generator (see the next page).

4) Biogas generators need to be kept at a constant temperature to keep the microorganisms respiring away.

5) There are two types of biogas generators — batch generators and continuous generators. These are explained on the next page.

6) Biogas can't be stored as a liquid (it needs too high a pressure), so it has to be used straight away — for heating, cooking, lighting, or to power a turbine to generate electricity.

Fuel Production Can Happen on a Large or Small Scale

1) Large-scale biogas generators are now being set up in a number of countries. Also, in some countries, small biogas generators are used to make enough gas for a village or a family to use in their cooking stoves and for heating and lighting.

2) Human waste, waste from keeping pigs, and food waste (e.g. kitchen scraps) can be digested by bacteria to produce biogas.

3) By-products are used to fertilise crops and gardens.

Anaerobics lesson — keep fit for bacteria...

Fascinating stuff, this biogas. It makes a lot of sense, I suppose, to get energy from rubbish, sewage and pig poop instead of leaving it all to rot naturally — which would mean all that lovely methane just wafting away into the atmosphere. Remember — anaerobic respiration makes biofuels.

Fuels from Microorganisms

Here's more than you could ever have wanted to know about that magic stuff, biogas.

Not All Biogas Generators Are the Same

There are two main types of biogas generator — batch generators and continuous generators.

Batch generators make biogas in small batches. They're manually loaded up with waste, which is left to digest, and the by-products are cleared away at the end of each session.

Continuous generators make biogas all the time. Waste is continuously fed in, and biogas is produced at a steady rate. Continuous generators are more suited to large-scale biogas projects.

The diagram on the right shows a simple biogas generator.

Whether it's a continuous or batch generator, it needs to have the following:

1) an inlet for waste material to be put in
2) an outlet for the digested material to be removed through
3) an outlet so that the biogas can be piped to where it is needed

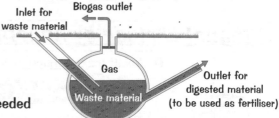
Inlet for waste material
Biogas outlet
Gas
Waste material
Outlet for digested material (to be used as fertiliser)

Four Factors to Consider When Designing a Generator:

When biogas generators are being designed, the following factors need to be considered:

COST: Continuous generators are more expensive than batch ones, because waste has to be mechanically pumped in and digested material mechanically removed all the time.

CONVENIENCE: Batch generators are less convenient because they have to be continually loaded, emptied and cleaned.

EFFICIENCY: Gas is produced most quickly at about 35 °C. If the temperature falls below this the gas production will be slower. Generators in some areas will need to be insulated or kept warm, e.g. by solar heaters. The generator shouldn't have any leaks or gas will be lost.

POSITION: The waste will smell during delivery, so generators should be sited away from homes. The generator is also best located fairly close to the waste source.

Using Biofuels Has Economic and Environmental Effects

1) Biofuels are a 'greener' alternative to fossil fuels. The carbon dioxide released into the atmosphere was taken in by plants which lived recently, so they're 'carbon neutral'.

2) The use of biofuels doesn't produce significant amounts of sulfur dioxide or nitrogen oxides, which cause acid rain.

3) Methane is a greenhouse gas and is one of those responsible for global warming. It's given off from untreated waste, which may be kept in farmyards or spread on agricultural land as fertiliser. Burning it as biogas means it's not released into the atmosphere.

CO_2 released
animal waste
Methane changed to CO_2
CO_2 absorbed in photosynthesis
Biogas generator

4) The raw material is cheap and readily available.

5) The digested material is a better fertiliser than undigested dung — so people can grow more crops.

6) In some developing rural communities women have to spend hours each day collecting wood for fuel. Biogas saves them this drudgery.

7) Biogas generators act as a waste disposal system, getting rid of human and animal waste that'd otherwise lie around, causing disease and polluting water supplies.

Don't sit under a cow — unless you want a pat on the head...

Biogas is fantastic. It gets rid of waste, makes a great fertiliser AND provides energy. Biogas isn't new though — before electricity, it was drawn from London's sewer pipes and burned in the street lights.

Using Microorganisms Safely

Microorganisms can be grown in a lab, but they need <u>certain conditions</u> to flourish.
Also, precautions must be taken to stop <u>unwanted</u> microorganisms growing as well.

Microorganisms Are Grown on Agar Jelly in a Petri Dish

1) Microorganisms are grown (cultured) in a "<u>culture medium</u>".

2) They need <u>carbohydrates</u> as an energy source, plus <u>mineral ions</u>,
   and sometimes supplementary <u>proteins</u> and <u>vitamins</u>.

3) These nutrients are usually added to the <u>agar jelly</u>.

4) Agar jelly can be <u>poured when hot</u>, and <u>sets when cold</u>.
   It's poured into shallow round plastic dishes called <u>Petri dishes</u>.

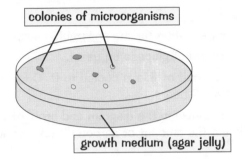

colonies of microorganisms

growth medium (agar jelly)

Equipment is Sterilised to Prevent Contamination

1) If equipment isn't sterilised, unwanted microorganisms in the
   growth medium will <u>grow</u> and <u>contaminate the end product</u>.

2) The unwanted microorganisms might make <u>harmful substances</u>,
   or cause <u>disease</u>.

3) Petri dishes and the <u>growth medium</u> must be sterilised before use.

4) <u>Inoculating loops</u> (used for transferring microorganisms to the
   growth medium) are <u>sterilised</u> by <u>passing them through a flame</u>.

5) The Petri dish must have a <u>lid</u> to stop any <u>microorganisms in the air</u>
   contaminating the culture. The lid should be <u>taped on</u>.

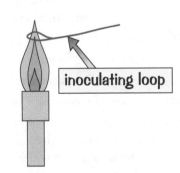

inoculating loop

The Temperature Must be Kept Fairly Low in School Labs

Pathogens are microorganisms
which cause disease.

In the <u>lab at school</u>, cultures of microorganisms are kept at about <u>25 °C</u>.
<u>Harmful pathogens</u> aren't likely to grow at this temperature.

In <u>industrial conditions</u>, cultures are incubated at <u>higher temperatures</u>
so that they can grow a lot faster.

Agar — my favourite jelly flavour after raspberry...

<u>Culture medium</u> = growth medium = liquid or jelly that the microorganisms are grown in. <u>Sorted</u>.
Microorganisms might be the perfect <u>pets</u>. You don't have to walk them, they won't get lonely and
they cost hardly anything to feed. But whatever you do, do <u>not</u> feed them after midnight.

Revision Summary for Biology 3(ii)

So you think you've learnt these pages on microorganisms, eh... Well, there's only one way to really find out. And you know what that is, I'll bet. It's obvious... I mean, there's a whole load of questions staring you in the face — chances are, it's got to involve those in some way. And sure enough, it does.
Just write down the answers to all these questions. Then go back over the section and see if you got any wrong. If you did, then you need a bit more revision, so go back and have another read of the section and then have another go. It's the best way to make sure you actually know your stuff.

1) What's the difference between spontaneous generation and biogenesis?

2) Describe three experiments that helped develop the theory of biogenesis.

3) What kind of microorganism is used in the manufacture of cheese?

4) In yoghurt-making, what's produced when the bacteria ferment the lactose in milk?

5) What type of microorganisms are yeasts?

6) What does "anaerobic" mean? Write an equation for the <u>anaerobic</u> respiration of glucose by yeast.

7) Write an equation for the <u>aerobic</u> respiration of glucose by yeast.

8)*Some yeast is added to 100 ml of water. Half of this is cooled to 0 °C for 2 hours and the other half is placed in a water bath at 90 °C for 2 hours.

Each sample is then placed in a flask as shown in the diagram and brought to 40 °C. 20 g of sugar is added to each flask and the amount of carbon dioxide produced by each is measured after an hour.

gas syringe

water
+ yeast
+ sugar

The sample that had been cooled to 0 °C produced 18 cm³ of carbon dioxide. The sample that had been heated did not produce any carbon dioxide.

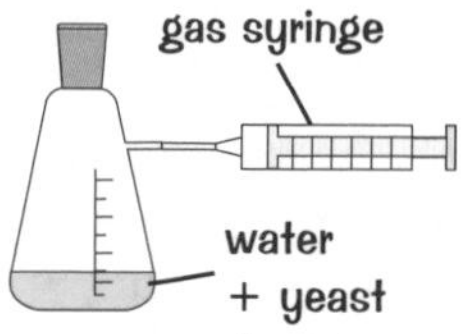

What conclusions can you draw from these results? How could you check the reliability of your results?

9) Explain what is meant by "malting".

10) Give four examples of conditions that are controlled inside an industrial fermenter.

11) What microorganism is the main source of mycoprotein?

12) What microorganism is used to make penicillin?

13) What is ethanol used for in some countries (apart from the obvious)?

14) What are the two main components of biogas?

15)* Loompah is a small village. It's very hot in the summer but freezing cold in winter. The villagers keep goats and cows. They also try to grow crops, but the soil isn't very fertile, so it's difficult. The villagers currently rely on wood for fuel for heating and cooking. There's not much of this around, so they spend a lot of time collecting it, preventing them from practising their nail-art.

a) How suitable do you think biogas would be for this village? Explain the advantages that using biogas would have for the village. What disadvantages or problems might there be?

b) Loompah starts using biogas and uses the digested material as fertiliser. They compare their crops to the crops grown by the village of Moompah, which uses normal manure as a fertiliser. Loompah's crops are bigger, so they conclude that the digested material is a better fertiliser than manure.

What do you think of the conclusion they've drawn?

16)* The data below shows the rate of biogas produced by a generator at various temperatures.

a) Draw a graph showing the temperature against biogas produced. Join the points with a smooth curve.

b) Using your graph, estimate the optimum temperature for biogas production.

c) How much biogas would you expect to be produced in 24 hours at 25 °C?

Temperature (°C)	10	20	30	40	50	60
Biogas produced in 1 hour (cm³)	6	32	54	78	50	18

17) What is a "culture medium"?

18) Why is it important to sterilise laboratory equipment before using it to culture microorganisms?

19) At what temperature are bacterial cultures usually incubated in the class lab? Is this hotter or colder than in industrial labs?

* Answers on page 76

History of the Periodic Table

We haven't always known as much about Chemistry as we do now. No sirree. Early chemists looked to try and understand <u>patterns</u> in the elements' properties to get a bit of understanding.

In the Early 1800s They Could Only Go on Atomic Mass

Until quite recently, there were <u>two</u> obvious ways to categorise elements:

1) Their <u>physical</u> and <u>chemical</u> <u>properties</u>	2) Their <u>Relative Atomic Mass</u>

1) Remember, they had <u>no idea</u> of <u>atomic structure</u> or of <u>protons</u> or <u>electrons</u>, so there was no such thing as <u>atomic number</u> to them. (It was only in the 20th century after protons and electrons were discovered that it was realised the elements were best arranged in order of <u>atomic number</u>.)

2) <u>Back then</u>, the only thing they could measure was <u>relative atomic mass</u>, and so the <u>known</u> elements were arranged <u>in order of atomic mass</u>. When this was done, a <u>periodic pattern</u> was noticed in the <u>properties</u> of the elements...

Newlands' Law of Octaves Was the First Good Effort

A chap called <u>Newlands</u> had the first good stab at arranging things more usefully in <u>1864</u>. He noticed that every <u>eighth</u> element had similar properties, and so he listed some of the known elements in rows of seven:

H	Li	Be	B	C	N	O
F	Na	Mg	Al	Si	P	S
Cl	K	Ca	Cr	Ti	Mn	Fe

These sets of eight were called <u>Newlands' Octaves</u>. Unfortunately the pattern <u>broke down</u> on the <u>third row</u>, with <u>transition metals</u> like titanium (Ti) and iron (Fe) messing it up.

It was because he left <u>no gaps</u> that his work was <u>ignored</u>. But he was getting <u>pretty close</u>, as you can see.

Newlands presented his ideas to the Chemical Society in 1865. But his work was criticised because:
1) His groups contained elements that didn't have <u>similar properties</u>, e.g. <u>carbon</u> and <u>titanium</u>.
2) He <u>mixed up metals and non-metals</u> e.g. <u>oxygen</u> and <u>iron</u>.
3) He <u>didn't leave any gaps</u> for elements that hadn't been discovered yet.

Dmitri Mendeleev Left Gaps and Predicted New Elements

1) In <u>1869</u>, <u>Dmitri Mendeleev</u> in Russia, armed with about 50 known elements, arranged them into his Table of Elements — with various <u>gaps</u> as shown.

2) Mendeleev put the elements in order of <u>atomic mass</u> (like Newlands did). But Mendeleev found he had to leave <u>gaps</u> in order to keep elements with <u>similar</u> <u>properties</u> in the same <u>vertical</u> <u>groups</u> — and he was prepared to leave some <u>very big gaps</u> in the first two rows before the transition metals come in on the <u>third</u> row.

Mendeleev's Table of the Elements

```
H
Li Be                               B  C  N  O  F
Na Mg                               Al Si P  S  Cl
K  Ca *  Ti V  Cr Mn Fe Co Ni Cu Zn *  *  As Se Br
Rb Sr Y  Zr Nb Mo *  Ru Rh Pd Ag Cd In Sn Sb Te I
Cs Ba *  *  Ta W  *  Os Ir Pt Au Hg Tl Pb Bi
```

3) The <u>gaps</u> were the really clever bit because they <u>predicted</u> the properties of so far <u>undiscovered elements</u>. When they were found and they <u>fitted</u> <u>the pattern</u> it was pretty smashing news for old Dmitri. The old rogue.

Julie Andrews' octaves — do, re, mi, fa, so, la, ti, do...

This is a good example of how science often progresses — even now. A scientist has a <u>basically good</u> (though incomplete) idea. Other scientists laugh and mock and generally deride. Eventually, the idea is modified a bit to take account of the <u>available evidence</u>, and voilà — into the textbooks it goes.

The Modern Periodic Table

Chemists were getting pretty close to producing something useful.
The big breakthrough came when the <u>structure</u> of the <u>atom</u> was understood a bit better.

Not **All Scientists** Thought the Periodic Table was Important

1) When the periodic table was first released, many scientists thought it was just a bit of <u>fun</u>. At that time, there wasn't all that much <u>evidence</u> to suggest that the elements really did fit together in that way — ideas don't get the scientific stamp of approval without evidence.

2) After Mendeleev released his work, <u>newly discovered elements</u> fitted into the <u>gaps</u> he left. This was convincing evidence in favour of the periodic table.

3) Once there was more evidence, many more scientists realised that the periodic table could be a <u>useful tool</u> for <u>predicting</u> properties of elements. It <u>really worked</u>.

4) In the late 19th century, scientists discovered protons, neutrons and electrons. The periodic table <u>matches up</u> very well to what's been discovered about the <u>structure</u> of the atom. Scientists now accept that it's a very important and useful <u>summary of atomic structure</u>.

The Modern Periodic Table **is Based on** Electronic Structure

When <u>electrons</u>, <u>protons</u> and <u>neutrons</u> were discovered, the periodic table was arranged in order of atomic (proton) numbers. All elements were put into <u>groups</u>.

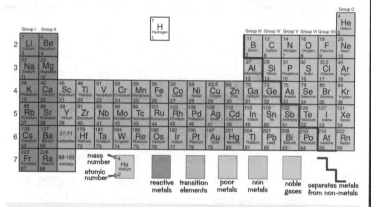

1) You can use the periodic table to work out the <u>detailed arrangement of electrons</u> in an atom of any element. Once you know the electron arrangement, you can predict the element's <u>chemical properties</u>.

2) Electrons in an atom are set out in <u>shells</u> which each correspond to an <u>energy level</u>.

3) The <u>maximum number</u> of electrons that can occupy each energy level is given by the simple formula $\underline{2 \times n^2}$, where n is the number of the energy level.

<u>Energy level 1</u> has a maximum of $2 \times 1^2 = \underline{2\ electrons}$
<u>Energy level 2</u> has a maximum of $2 \times 2^2 = \underline{8\ electrons}$
<u>Energy level 3</u> has a maximum of $2 \times 3^2 = \underline{18\ electrons}$

4) Apart from the transition metals, elements in the same group have the <u>same number of electrons</u> in their <u>highest occupied energy level</u> — e.g. Group 6 all have 6 electrons in the highest energy level. The transition metals fill up their electron shells in their own <u>slightly peculiar way</u> — see p23.

5) The positive charge of the nucleus attracts electrons and holds them in place. The <u>further</u> from the nucleus the electron is, the <u>less the attraction</u>.

6) The attraction of the nucleus is <u>even less</u> when there are a lot of <u>inner electrons</u>. Inner electrons "get in the way" of the nuclear charge, reducing the attraction. This effect is known as <u>shielding</u>.

7) The combination of <u>increased distance</u> and <u>increased shielding</u> means that an electron in a higher energy level is <u>more easily lost</u> because there's <u>less attraction</u> from the nucleus holding it in place. That's why <u>Group 1 metals</u> get <u>more reactive</u> as you go down the group.

8) <u>Increased distance</u> and <u>shielding</u> also means that a higher energy level is <u>less likely to gain an electron</u> — there's less attraction from the nucleus pulling electrons into the atom. That's why <u>Group 7 elements</u> get <u>less reactive</u> going down the group.

It's worth taking a minute (or several) to get this in your head.

You are now approaching Group III — mind the gap...

In the exam, you can be asked factual questions like "<u>Use electron structure to explain why Cs is more reactive than Na</u>" or ideas questions like "<u>Why did scientists accept the periodic table as important?</u>", or both. So there's no excuse for not <u>learning</u> what's on the page. Even though there is rather a lot of it...

Group I — The Alkali Metals

They're all silvery solids. And they're called 'alkali metals' because their hydroxides dissolve in water to give an alkaline solution. Simple.

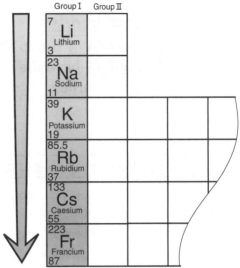

Learn These Trends:

As you go DOWN Group I, the alkali metals become:

1) **BIGGER ATOMS**

   ...because there's one extra full shell of electrons for each row you go down.

2) **MORE REACTIVE**

   ...because the outer electron is more easily lost, because it's further from the nucleus.

3) **HIGHER DENSITY**

   ...because the atoms have more mass.
   The three at the top are less dense than water.

4) **LOWER MELTING POINT**

5) **LOWER BOILING POINT**

1) The Alkali Metals are Very Reactive

They have to be stored in oil and handled with forceps (they burn the skin).

2) They are: Lithium, Sodium, Potassium and a Couple More

Know those three names real well. They may also mention rubidium and caesium.

3) The Alkali Metals All Have ONE Outer Electron

This makes them very reactive and gives them all similar properties.

4) The Alkali Metals All Form 1⁺ Ions

They are keen to lose their one outer electron to form a 1^+ ion:

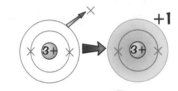

5) The Alkali Metals Always Form Ionic Compounds

They are so keen to lose the outer electron there's no way they'd consider sharing, so covalent bonding is out of the question.

6) Reaction with Water Produces Hydrogen Gas

1) When lithium, sodium or potassium are put in water, they react very vigorously.

2) They move around the surface, fizzing furiously.

3) They produce hydrogen. Potassium gets hot enough to ignite it. A lighted splint will indicate hydrogen by producing the notorious "squeaky pop" as the H_2 ignites.

4) They form a hydroxide in solution, i.e. aqueous OH⁻ ions.

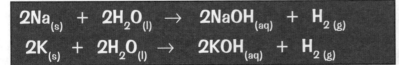

$$2Na_{(s)} + 2H_2O_{(l)} \rightarrow 2NaOH_{(aq)} + H_{2\,(g)}$$
$$2K_{(s)} + 2H_2O_{(l)} \rightarrow 2KOH_{(aq)} + H_{2\,(g)}$$

The solution becomes alkaline, which changes the colour of the pH indicator to purple.

5 trends and 6 properties — not much to learn at all...

I'm no gambler, but I'd put money on a question like this in the exam: "Using your knowledge of the Group I metals, describe what would happen if a piece of caesium were put into water." Just use what you know about the other Group I metals... you're going to get H_2, and a pretty violent reaction.

Group VII — The Halogens

The 'trend thing' happens in Group VII as well — that shouldn't come as a surprise.
But some of the trends are kind of the opposite of the Group I trends. Remember that.

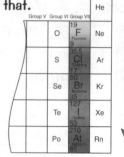

Learn These Trends:

As you go DOWN Group VII,
the HALOGENS have the
following properties:

1) LESS REACTIVE
2) HIGHER MELTING POINT
3) HIGHER BOILING POINT

1) The Halogens are All Non-metals with Coloured Vapours

Fluorine is a very reactive, poisonous yellow gas.
Chlorine is a fairly reactive, poisonous dense green gas.
Bromine is a dense, poisonous, red-brown volatile liquid.
Iodine is a dark grey crystalline solid or a purple vapour.

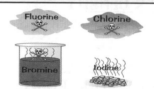

2) They All Form Molecules Which are Pairs of Atoms:

 F_2 $\quad$ Cl_2 $\quad$ Br_2 $\quad$ I_2

3) The Halogens Do Both Ionic and Covalent Bonding

The halogens form 1⁻ ions when they bond with metals: F^-, Cl^-, Br^- and I^- (as in Na^+Cl^- or $Fe^{3+}Br^-_3$).
But they form covalent bonds with non-metals to form molecules like these:

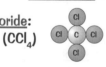 Carbon tetrachloride:
(CCl_4)

 Hydrogen chloride:
(HCl)

4) The Halogens React with Metals to Form Salts

They react with most metals, including iron and
aluminium, to form salts (or 'metal halides').

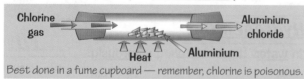

Chlorine gas → Aluminium chloride
Heat — Aluminium
Best done in a fume cupboard — remember, chlorine is poisonous.

$$2Al_{(s)} + 3Cl_{2(g)} \rightarrow 2AlCl_{3(s)}$$
(Aluminium chloride)

$$2Fe_{(s)} + 3Br_{2(g)} \rightarrow 2FeBr_{3(s)}$$
(Iron(III) bromide)

5) More Reactive Halogens Will Displace Less Reactive Ones

Chlorine can displace bromine and iodine from a solution of bromide or iodide.
Bromine will also displace iodine because of the trend in reactivity.

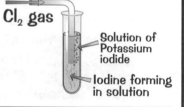

Cl_2 gas
Solution of Potassium iodide
Iodine forming in solution

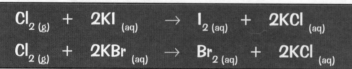

$$Cl_{2(g)} + 2KI_{(aq)} \rightarrow I_{2(aq)} + 2KCl_{(aq)}$$

$$Cl_{2(g)} + 2KBr_{(aq)} \rightarrow Br_{2(aq)} + 2KCl_{(aq)}$$

Oooh, only 3 trends and 5 properties — even easier...

Once more, you don't have to be a mind-reader to be able to guess the kind of thing they're going to
ask you in the exam. My money's on something to do with displacement reactions — will iodine
displace bromine from some compound or other, for instance. Learn the facts... just learn the facts.

Transition Elements

Transition elements make up the big clump of metals in the middle of the periodic table.
Transition elements (or transition metals) are typical metals, and have the properties you
would expect of a 'proper' metal:

1) They're good conductors of heat and electricity.

2) They're very dense, strong and shiny.

3) Transition metals are much less reactive than Group I metals — they don't react very much with water or oxygen, for example.

4) They're also much denser, stronger and harder than the Group I metals, and have much higher melting points (except for mercury, which is a liquid at room temperature). E.g. iron melts at 1500 °C, copper at 1100 °C and zinc at 400 °C.

Here they are, right in the middle of Group II and Group III.

45 Sc Scandium 21	48 Ti Titanium 22	51 V Vanadium 23	52 Cr Chromium 24	55 Mn Manganese 25	56 Fe Iron 26	59 Co Cobalt 27	59 Ni Nickel 28	63.5 Cu Copper 29	65 Zn Zinc 30
89 Y Yttrium 39	91 Zr Zirconium 40	93 Nb Niobium 41	96 Mo Molybdenum 42	98 Tc Technetium 43	101 Ru Ruthenium 44	103 Rh Rhodium 45	106 Pd Palladium 46	108 Ag Silver 47	201 Cd Cadmium 48
57-71 Lanthanides	178.5 Hf Hafnium 72	181 Ta Tantalum 73	184 W Tungsten 74	186 Re Rhenium 75	190 Os Osmium 76	192 Ir Iridium 77	195 Pt Platinum 78	197 Au Gold 79	201 Hg Mercury 80
89-103 Actinides									

Transition Metals Often Have More Than One Ion, e.g. Fe^{2+}, Fe^{3+}

Two other examples are copper: Cu^+ and Cu^{2+} and chromium: Cr^{2+}, Cr^{3+} and Cr^{6+}

The different ions usually form different-coloured compounds too:
Fe^{2+} ions usually give green compounds, whereas Fe^{3+} ions usually form red/brown compounds (e.g. rust).

The Compounds are Very Colourful

1) The compounds are colourful due to the transition metal ion they contain, e.g.
Potassium chromate(VI) is yellow. Potassium manganate(VII) is purple. Copper(II) sulfate is blue.

2) The colour of people's hair and also the colours in gemstones, like blue sapphires and green emeralds, and the colours in pottery glazes are all due to transition metals.
And weathered copper is a lovely colourful green.

Transition Metals and Their Compounds All Make Good Catalysts

1) Iron is the catalyst used in the Haber process for making ammonia.

2) Manganese(IV) oxide is a good catalyst for the decomposition of hydrogen peroxide.

3) Nickel is useful for turning oils into fats for making margarine.

Their Properties are Due to the Way Their Electron Shells Fill

1) In an atom, as you get further from the nucleus, energy levels get closer together until they start to overlap. This first happens between energy levels 3 and 4. It affects the way the electron shells fill.

2) Potassium has 19 electrons — but the 19th electron goes into the 4th energy level, not the 3rd. The electron arrangement's 2, 8, 8, 1. Same thing with the next element, calcium — which is 2, 8, 8, 2.

3) The next ten elements (the transition metals) put their electrons into the overlapping 3rd energy level until it's full.

You don't need to know how this causes their various properties, just that it does.

Sc	Ti	V	Cr	Mn	Fe	Co	Ni	Cu	Zn
2,8,9,2	2,8,10,2	2,8,11,2	2,8,13,1	2,8,13,2	2,8,14,2	2,8,15,2	2,8,16,2	2,8,18,1	2,8,18,2

(Chromium (Cr) and copper (Cu) fill up a bit differently. The reason's complicated (A2-level), so for now just learn the numbers.)

Shiny metals, pretty colours, electrons — we've got it all...

Most common everyday metals are transition elements — for example, iron, nickel, copper, silver, gold, tantalum (spiders ought to be made of this), and so on. There are a lot of facts to learn here about colour and melting points. Learn the weird fact about electron shells and impress the examiners.

Acids and Alkalis

Theories about what makes an acid an acid, and a base a base, have <u>evolved</u> a bit over the years.

Arrhenius Said Acids Release Hydrogen Ions in Water

1) A guy called Arrhenius studied acids and bases in water. His theory was that when mixed with <u>water</u>, all acids release <u>hydrogen ions</u>, H^+ (an H^+ ion is a proton). For example,

$$HCl\ (g) + water \longrightarrow H^+\ (aq) + Cl^-\ (aq)$$
$$H_2SO_4\ (l) + water \longrightarrow 2H^+\ (aq) + SO_4^{2-}\ (aq)$$

But HCl <u>doesn't</u> release hydrogen ions <u>until</u> it meets water — so hydrogen chloride gas isn't an acid.

2) He also said that <u>alkalis</u> form OH^- ions (<u>hydroxide</u> ions) when in <u>water</u>.

E.g.
$$Ammonia: NH_3(g) + H_2O\ (l) \longrightarrow NH_4^+(aq) + OH^-(aq)$$

Not all bases <u>dissolve</u> in water, but those that do are called <u>alkalis</u>.

3) This idea worked pretty well, <u>but</u> it only worked for acids and bases that dissolved in <u>water</u>. However, <u>ammonia gas</u> can react as a base even when it isn't dissolved in water, which was one reason why these ideas weren't immediately accepted. (A hypothesis is always less likely to be accepted when there are lots of <u>exceptions</u> which the hypothesis can't explain.)

4) Also, back in the 1880s when Arrhenius first suggested that molecules ionise in water, many scientists didn't believe it was <u>possible</u>. <u>Charged subatomic particles</u> hadn't been <u>discovered yet</u>, so the idea of charged ions seemed very <u>strange</u>. Scientists couldn't imagine how Cl^- could be different from Cl_2 gas.

Lowry and Brønsted Said Acids Are Proton Donors

1) <u>Lowry and Brønsted</u> (working separately) made things a bit more general. They came up with definitions that work for both <u>soluble</u> and <u>insoluble</u> bases:

<u>Acids</u> release H^+ ions — i.e. they're <u>proton donors</u>.
<u>Bases</u> accept H^+ ions — i.e. they're <u>proton acceptors</u>.

In fact, it'd be more accurate to say that acids have their proton <u>taken away</u> from them.

2) The ideas of Lowry and Brønsted were <u>readily accepted</u> because they explained the behaviour of acids and bases in solvents other than water. Also, they were an <u>adaptation</u> of an idea which <u>already kind of worked</u>. When Arrhenius came up with his idea it was <u>totally new</u>, so people took more convincing.

Protons Are Hydrated in Water

Anyway... for a substance to act as an acid or as a base, you <u>usually</u> need <u>water</u>. This is what happens...

In acidic solutions:

The acid molecules <u>dissociate</u>, releasing lots of $\underline{H^+\ ions}$.

These H^+ ions (protons) become <u>hydrated</u> (surrounded by water molecules). The protons are now given the fancy name '<u>hydrated protons</u>' and can be represented by '$\underline{H^+(aq)}$'.
And it's these hydrated protons that make acids acidic, if you like.

In basic solutions:

Water molecules can <u>dissociate</u> into H^+ and OH^- ions, although they almost never do in pure water. But, some base molecules, like ammonia (NH_3), can <u>take hydrogen ions</u> from water, causing more molecules to dissociate, and leaving an excess of OH^- ions behind. Other bases, like potassium hydroxide (KOH), <u>release hydroxide ions</u> straight into the solution.

Lowry, what a guy — explaining acids AND painting factories...

Here's another example of how scientific knowledge progresses — lots of people contributing ideas to fit the <u>available evidence</u>. Some ideas are better than others, but usually the rubbish ones are quickly forgotten and you don't have to learn about those (e.g. acidic behaviour being due to magic pixies).

Acids, Alkalis and Titration

Like a character in a soap and their evil twin, acids and bases are opposites. And they neutralise each other — acids and bases, I mean. (But I reckon this could work for evil twins as well.)

Acids Can Be Strong or Weak

1) Strong acids (e.g. sulfuric, hydrochloric and nitric) ionise almost completely in water. This means almost every hydrogen atom is released to become a hydrated proton (so there are loads of $H^+(aq)$ ions).

2) Weak acids (e.g. ethanoic, citric, carbonic) ionise only very slightly — only some of the hydrogen atoms in the compound are released — so only small numbers of $H^+(aq)$ ions are formed.

For example,

$$\underline{\text{Strong acid}}: HCl + water \longrightarrow H^+ + Cl^-$$

$$\underline{\text{Weak acid}}: H_2CO_3 + water \rightleftharpoons H^+ + HCO_3^-$$

Note the 'reversible reaction' symbol for a weak acid.

3) The pH of an acid or alkali is a measure of the concentration of $H^+(aq)$ ions in a solution. Strong acids typically have a pH of about 1 or 2, while the pH of a weak acid might be 4, 5 or 6.

4) The pH of an acid or alkali can be measured with a pH meter or with universal indicator paper (or can be estimated by seeing how fast a sample reacts with, say, magnesium).

5) There are strong and weak alkalis too. The hydroxides of sodium and potassium, KOH and NaOH, are strong (typically pH 13 or 14), while ammonia solution is a weak alkali (pH 9-10).

Titrations are Used to Find Out Concentrations

1) Titrations allow you to find out exactly how much acid is needed to neutralise a quantity of alkali (or vice versa).

2) You put some alkali in a flask, along with some indicator. The indicator used depends on the strengths of the acid and alkali:

- Phenolphthalein is used for a weak acid and strong alkali
- Methyl orange is used for a strong acid and weak alkali
- If both the acid and alkali are strong any acid-base indicator can be used.

3) Add the acid, a bit at a time, to the alkali using a burette — giving the flask a regular swirl. Go especially slowly (a drop at a time) when you think the alkali's almost neutralised.

4) The indicator changes colour when all the alkali has been neutralised, e.g. phenolphthalein is pink in alkalis, but colourless in acids.

5) Record the amount of acid used to neutralise the alkali. It's best to repeat this process a few times, making sure you get (pretty much) the same answer each time.

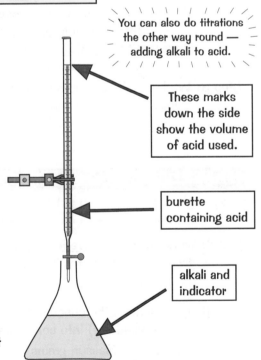

You can also do titrations the other way round — adding alkali to acid.

These marks down the side show the volume of acid used.

burette containing acid

alkali and indicator

If you can spell phenolphthalein, you deserve a GCSE...

Well, there you have it — lots of info about acids and bases. And while at first glance it might look dull, it'll probably seem dull when you read it again. But no matter — it's got to be understood.
There's a little bit at the end there that's pretty vital when you do any experiment — the bit about repeating the process to check your results. It's all to do with making sure your results are reliable. If you get the same result a number of times, you can have more faith in it than if it's a one-off.

Titration Calculations

I expect you're wondering what you can do with the results from a titration experiment (who wouldn't be). Well, you'll be relieved to know that they can be used to <u>calculate concentrations</u> of acids or alkalis.

You Might Be Asked to Calculate the Concentration

In the exam you might be given the results of a titration experiment and asked to calculate the concentration of the acid when you know the concentration of the alkali (or vice versa).

Example 1: If they ask for concentration in MOLES per dm³

Say you start off with <u>25 cm³</u> of sodium hydroxide in your flask, and you know that its concentration is <u>0.1 moles per dm³</u>.

You then find from your titration that it takes <u>30 cm³</u> of sulfuric acid (whose concentration you don't know) to neutralise the sodium hydroxide.

You can work out the <u>concentration</u> of the acid in <u>moles per dm³</u>.

Concentration = moles ÷ volume, so you can make a handy formula triangle.

Concentration (in mol/dm³) — n — Number of moles — Volume (in dm³) — One dm³ is a litre — $c \times V$

Cover up the thing you're trying to find — then what's left is the formula you need to use.

Step 1: Work out how many <u>moles</u> of the "known" substance you have:

Number of moles = concentration × volume
= 0.1 mol/dm³ × (25 / 1000) dm³ = <u>0.0025 moles of NaOH</u>

Remember: 1000 cm³ = 1 dm³

Use the formula triangle if it helps.

Step 2: Write down the <u>balanced equation</u> of the reaction...

$$2NaOH + H_2SO_4 \longrightarrow Na_2SO_4 + 2H_2O$$

...and work out how many <u>moles</u> of the "<u>unknown</u>" stuff you must have had.

Using the equation, you can see that for every <u>two moles</u> of sodium hydroxide you had...
...there was just <u>one mole</u> of sulfuric acid.
So if you had <u>0.0025 moles</u> of sodium hydroxide...
...you must have had 0.0025 ÷ 2 = <u>0.00125 moles of sulfuric acid.</u>

Step 3: Work out the concentration of the "unknown" stuff.
Concentration = number of moles ÷ volume
= 0.00125 mol ÷ (30 / 1000) dm³ = 0.041666... mol/dm³
= <u>0.0417 mol/dm³</u>

Don't forget to put the units.

Example 2: If they ask for concentration in GRAMS per dm³

They might ask you to find out the acid concentration in <u>grams per cubic decimetre</u> (<u>grams per litre</u>). If they do, don't panic — you just need another formula triangle.

Step 1: Work out the <u>relative formula mass</u> for the acid (you should be given the relative atomic masses, e.g. H = 1, S = 32, O = 16):

So, $H_2SO_4 = (1 \times 2) + 32 + (16 \times 4) = 98$

Step 2: Convert the concentration in <u>moles</u> (that you've already worked out) into concentration in <u>grams</u>. So, in 1 dm³:

Use non-rounded answers in workings.

Mass in grams = moles × relative formula mass
= 0.041666... × 98 = 4.08333... g
So the <u>concentration in g/dm³ = 4.08 g/dm³</u>

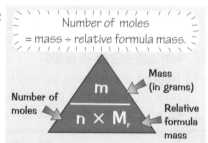

Number of moles = mass ÷ relative formula mass.

Number of moles — m — Mass (in grams) — $n \times M_r$ — Relative formula mass

Need practice, you do — mmmm...

Scary. But if you get enough practice at these questions, then the fear will evaporate and you can tackle them with a smile on your face and a spring in your step. By the way, don't be baffled by dm³ — it's just an overly complicated way of saying "<u>litre</u>", that's all. So "<u>moles per dm³</u>" means "<u>moles per litre</u>".

Water

Without water, there'd be no swimming, no cups of tea, no power showers — a nightmare.
Plus you wouldn't even exist — you need water to live.

The Water Cycle Means Water is Endlessly Recycled

This stuff about the water cycle probably won't come as a complete surprise...

1) The Sun causes evaporation of water from the sea. The water vapour is then carried upwards as the warm air rises.

2) As the water vapour rises it cools — due to the general cooling of the lower part of the atmosphere at higher altitudes. This fall in temperature means the water condenses to form clouds.

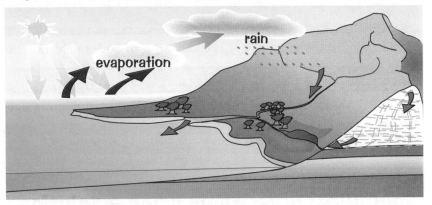

3) When the condensed droplets get too big they fall as rain.

4) Then the water runs back to the sea. However it gets back to the sea, at some stage it's going to come into contact with the rocks on (or underneath) the ground — meaning that water in different places will dissolve different minerals (see page 29 for more about this).

5) Then the cycle starts over again.

Water's a Solvent — It Dissolves Many Other Chemicals

So many substances dissolve in water that sometimes water is called the universal solvent.

1) Water dissolves most ionic compounds. Water molecules start to surround the ions, and disrupt the ionic bonding, so the solid structure of the ionic compound gradually falls apart.

2) Water molecules are polar, remember — they've got a positive hydrogen side and a negative oxygen side. The slightly negative side attracts the positive ions and the slightly positive side attracts the negative ions.

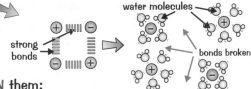

3) The following ionic compounds dissolve in water — LEARN them:

   a) Salts of SODIUM (Na), POTASSIUM (K) or AMMONIUM (NH_4). ALL of these dissolve.

   b) NITRATES (NO_3). ALL of these dissolve.

   c) CHLORIDES (Cl), except for silver and lead.

   d) SULFATES (SO_4), except for barium and lead. Calcium sulfate is only slightly soluble.

   Plus there are one or two others, but you don't need to know about them.

4) Some substances that exist as small molecules are soluble in water, e.g. CO_2, SO_2 and Cl_2. Many covalent compounds don't dissolve — they don't form ions and their molecules are too big.

Water in the form of streams, rivers and rain dissolves a lot of substances that it comes into contact with — e.g. salts from rocks, fertilisers from fields, and gases in the atmosphere, such as sulfur dioxide from power stations and car exhausts. Sulfur dioxide dissolves to form an acid, which can fall as acid rain.

Water is essential for life. Life is a complicated bunch of chemical reactions, which largely take place in solution in water. Many important biological chemicals like sugars, salts and amino acids dissolve in water.

Round and round and round it goes...

You've more than likely seen the water cycle before. But it's really important to think about what the water comes into contact with as it goes round — what it dissolves will affect the properties of the water. You'll have to learn the rules for which ionic compounds dissolve, I'm afraid. No easy shortcuts.

Solubility

Something is <u>soluble</u> if it <u>dissolves</u> — like <u>sugar</u> when you put it in tea (hurrah).
Something is <u>insoluble</u> if it <u>doesn't dissolve</u> — like <u>sand</u> when you put it in tea (boo, hiss).

Solubility — *Learn the Proper Definitions*

The <u>solubility</u> of a substance in a given solvent is the number of <u>grams of the solute</u> (usually a solid) that dissolve in <u>100 g of the solvent</u> (the liquid) at a particular <u>temperature</u>.

E.g. at <u>room temperature (20 °C)</u>, about 36 g of sodium chloride (NaCl) will dissolve in 100 g of water.

The solubility of (solid) <u>solutes</u> usually <u>increases with temperature</u>.

E.g. at <u>60 °C</u>, about 37 g of sodium chloride (NaCl) will dissolve in 100 g of water.

A <u>saturated solution</u> is one that cannot hold any more solid <u>at that temperature</u> — and you have to be able to see <u>solid</u> on the bottom to be certain that it's saturated.

Solubility Curves *Show When a Solution is Saturated*

1) A <u>solubility curve</u> plots the <u>mass of solute</u> dissolved in a saturated solution at <u>various temperatures</u>.

2) The solubility of most solids <u>increases</u> as the temperature <u>increases</u>.

3) This means that <u>cooling</u> a saturated solution will usually cause some solid to <u>crystallise out</u> — that means it <u>separates</u> from the solution.

4) The <u>mass</u> of <u>crystals</u> formed by <u>cooling</u> a solution a certain amount can be calculated from a solubility curve...

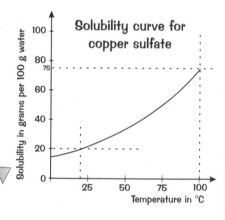

Solubility curve for copper sulfate

Draw lines perpendicular to both axes through the temperatures in the question, then subtract the smaller mass from the larger — that difference will precipitate out on cooling.
This graph is for 100 g of water — so if you had 1000 g of water instead, you'd just multiply your answer by 10. Ain't so bad.

<u>Example</u>: What mass of solid copper sulfate will crystallise when a saturated solution containing 100 g of water is cooled from 100 °C to 20 °C? <u>Answer</u>: 75 g – 20 g = <u>55 g</u>

All Gases are Soluble — *to Some Extent, Anyway*

1) "<u>Chlorine water</u>" is (unsurprisingly) a <u>solution</u> of <u>chlorine gas</u> in <u>water</u>. It's used as <u>bleach</u> in the paper and textile industries, and also to <u>sterilise</u> water supplies (it <u>kills</u> bacteria).

2) The <u>amount</u> of gas that dissolves depends on the <u>pressure</u> of the gas above it — the <u>higher</u> the pressure, the <u>more gas</u> that dissolves.

   Fizzy drinks initially contain a <u>lot</u> of carbon dioxide dissolved in water (carbonated water).
   But when you take the cap off, the pressure's <u>released</u> and a lot of CO_2 fizzes <u>out</u> of solution.

3) But... gases become <u>less soluble</u> as the <u>temperature</u> of the solvent <u>increases</u>, which is exactly the <u>opposite</u> of solids.

   Aquatic life needs dissolved <u>oxygen</u>, but the <u>oxygen levels</u> in <u>rivers</u> can be lowered by <u>pollution</u> and a <u>rise in temperature</u> (caused by <u>warm water</u> discharged from towns and industry), causing problems.

Don't let your head get saturated with facts — *there's more to go...*

Solubility graphs make for an obvious exam question — just check the <u>mass</u> of water in the question.
Now think — if you heat a pan of lemonade, would it get more fizzy, or less... Well, as the temperature goes up, less CO_2 dissolves, so it'll be less fizzy, and so a poor alternative to a cup of tea on a cold day.

Hard Water

The water in your part of the country might be <u>hard</u> or <u>soft</u> — it depends on the rocks rainwater passes through on its way to you. With soft water, you get a nice lather with soap. Not so with hard water...

Hard Water Makes Scum and Scale

1) <u>Hard water</u> won't easily form a <u>lather</u> with soap (non-soap detergents aren't affected) — you get a <u>nasty scum</u> instead. So to get a decent lather you need to use more soap.
The problem is the 'hardness minerals' (see below) in the hard water reacting with the soap.

2) Hard water also forms furring or <u>scale</u> (mostly calcium carbonate) on the insides of pipes, boilers and kettles. Badly scaled-up pipes and boilers reduce the efficiency of heating systems, and may need to be <u>replaced</u> — all of which costs money. Scale can even <u>eventually block pipes</u>.

3) <u>Scale</u> is also a bit of a <u>thermal insulator</u>. This means that a <u>kettle</u> with scale on the <u>heating element</u> takes <u>longer to boil</u> than a <u>clean</u> non-scaled-up kettle — so it becomes <u>less efficient</u>.

4) Worst of all, hard water can also cause a <u>horrible scum</u> to form on the <u>surface of tea</u>.

Hardness is Caused by Ca^{2+} and Mg^{2+} ions

1) Most hard water is hard because it contains lots of <u>calcium</u> and <u>magnesium</u> ions.
You get hard water in certain areas because of the type of rocks there.
Hardness often comes from <u>limestone</u>, <u>chalk</u> and <u>gypsum</u>.

2) For instance, rain falling on some types of rocks can dissolve <u>magnesium sulfate</u> (which is soluble), and <u>calcium sulfate</u> (which is also soluble, though only a bit).

3) Other calcium and magnesium salts come from a reaction. When <u>carbon dioxide</u> from the air <u>dissolves</u> in <u>rainwater</u>, you get <u>carbonic acid</u> ($CO_2 + H_2O \rightarrow H_2CO_3$) — so rainwater is slightly <u>acidic</u>.
Then if there's <u>calcium carbonate</u> ($CaCO_3$) in the rocks, <u>calcium hydrogencarbonate</u> is formed ($H_2CO_3 + CaCO_3 \rightarrow Ca(HCO_3)_2$), which is <u>soluble</u>. Similarly with rocks containing $MgCO_3$.

Hard Water Isn't All Bad

1) Ca^{2+} ions are good for healthy <u>teeth</u> and <u>bones</u>.

2) And scale inside pipes forms a <u>protective coating</u>. It stops poisonous <u>metal ions</u>, e.g. <u>Pb^{2+}</u> and <u>Cu^{2+}</u> (from lead and copper pipes) getting into <u>drinking water</u>. It also protects iron pipes from <u>rust</u>.

Remove Hardness by Removing Dissolved Ca^{2+} and Mg^{2+} Ions

1) By adding <u>sodium carbonate</u>.
The carbonate ions join onto the calcium or magnesium ions and make an <u>insoluble precipitate</u>.

e.g. $\boxed{Ca^{2+}(aq) + CO_3^{2-}(aq) \rightarrow CaCO_3(s)}$

2) By '<u>ion exchange columns</u>'. Sometimes a water supply is fed through an ion exchange column to remove the hardness. These clever bits of chemistry have lots of <u>sodium ions</u> (or <u>hydrogen ions</u>) and 'exchange' them for calcium or magnesium ions in the water that runs through them.

e.g. $\boxed{Na_2Resin(s) + Ca^{2+}(aq) \rightarrow CaResin(s) + 2Na^+(aq)}$ ('Resin' is a huge insoluble resin molecule.)

3) Scale is mainly just <u>calcium carbonate</u>, and can be dissolved by <u>acid</u>.
Most descaling products that you buy to clean your kettle out are some kind of acid.

And if the water's really hard, you can chip your teeth...

Hard water — good thing or bad thing... Well, it provides minerals that are good for health, but it creates an awful lot of <u>unnecessary expense</u>. In hard water areas, you need more soap to get a lather, it takes longer (and therefore more 'leccy') to boil water (as heating elements get furred up), and you need to get your pipes replaced more often. All in all, it's a bit of a drag. But you <u>still need to learn it</u>.

Water Quality

It's easy to take water for granted... turn on the tap, and there it is — nice, clean water. The water you drink's been round the block a few times — so there's some <u>fancy chemistry</u> needed to make it drinkable.

Drinking Water Needs to Be Good Quality

Water's essential for life, but it must be free of <u>poisonous salts</u> (e.g. phosphates and nitrates) and harmful <u>microorganisms</u>. Microorganisms in water can cause <u>diseases</u> such as cholera and dysentery.

Most of our drinking water comes from <u>reservoirs</u>. Water flows into reservoirs from <u>rivers</u> and <u>groundwater</u> — water companies choose to build reservoirs where there's a good supply of <u>clean water</u>. Government agencies keep a close eye on <u>pollution</u> in reservoirs, rivers and groundwater.

<u>Water from reservoirs goes to the water treatment works for treatment</u>:

1) The water passes though a <u>mesh screen</u> to remove big bits like twigs.

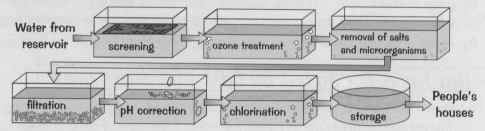

2) Next, it's treated with <u>ozone or chlorine</u> to <u>kill</u> microorganisms.

3) Chemicals are added to make solids and microorganisms <u>stick together</u> and fall to the bottom. Sometimes iron is added to remove dissolved phosphates. Bacteria are used to remove nitrates.

4) The water is <u>filtered</u> through gravel beds to remove all the solids. <u>Nasty tastes and odours</u> can also be removed by passing the water through "<u>activated carbon</u>" filters or with "<u>carbon slurry</u>".

5) The <u>pH is corrected</u> if the water is too acidic or too alkaline.

6) Water is <u>chlorinated</u> to kill off any harmful <u>microorganisms</u> left.

To <u>monitor water quality</u>, water companies take <u>samples</u> of water — from the water entering the treatment works right though to the taps in consumers' houses.

Some people <u>still aren't satisfied</u>. They buy filters that contain <u>carbon</u> or <u>silver</u> to remove substances from their tap water. Carbon in the filters removes <u>chlorine taste</u> and silver is supposed to kill bugs.

Some people in hard water areas buy <u>water softeners</u> which contain <u>ion exchange resins</u> (see page 29).

<u>Totally pure water</u> with <u>nothing</u> dissolved in it can be produced by <u>distillation</u> — boiling water to make steam and condensing the steam. This process is too <u>expensive</u> to produce tap water — bags of energy would be needed to boil all the water we use. Distilled water is used in <u>chemistry labs</u>.

Clean Water is Essential for Life

You'd use pure water to make a solution of (say) KBr, because you wouldn't want any other ions mucking it up.

1) Not everyone has clean water. The <u>World Health Organisation</u> (WHO) and the United Nations estimated in 2000 that <u>a billion people</u> in the world don't have access to <u>clean drinking water</u>.

2) In many developing countries it's very <u>expensive</u> to get clean water. Some people in developing countries live in isolated rural areas, and have to walk miles to get <u>any</u> water at all.

3) It's a fact that the <u>biggest increases in life expectancy</u> in most countries' histories (including the UK's) are linked with the ability to supply clean water — not medicine or anything like that. It's that vital. In November 2004 the <u>WHO</u> said that improving drinking water quality could <u>reduce diarrhoeal disease</u> by up to 40%. Currently, 1.8 million people each year die of diarrhoeal diseases (e.g. cholera).

4) Some water purifying processes can <u>damage the environment</u>, which is worth bearing in mind.

The water you drink has been through 7 people already...

Well, it's possible. It's also possible that the water you're drinking used to be part of the Atlantic Ocean. Or it could have been drunk by Alexander the Great. Or part of an Alpine glacier. Aye, it gets about a bit, does water. And remember... tap water isn't pure — but it's <u>drinkable</u>, and that's the main thing.

Revision Summary for Chemistry 3(i)

Bit of a mixed bag — one minute you're pondering the periodic table, the next you're worrying about how many millions of people are without clean drinking water. The one thing that's constant and unchanging is the need to learn it all for the exam you've got coming up. So test yourself on these little beauties.

1) Before 1800, how were elements classified?

2) Give two reasons why Newlands' Octaves were criticised.

3) Why did Mendeleev leave gaps in his Table of Elements?

4) How many electrons can fit into energy level 2? How many in energy level 3?

5) What is shielding?

6) Explain why Group 7 elements get less reactive as you go down the group from fluorine to iodine.

7) As you go down Group I, what's the trend in: a) reactivity, b) density, c) melting point?

8) Write down the balanced equation for the reaction between sodium and water.

9) Describe the physical properties of: a) chlorine, b) bromine, c) iodine.

10) Do halogens do covalent bonding, ionic bonding, or both?

11)* Write down the balanced equation for the reaction between iron and chlorine gas.

12) Will the following reactions occur: a) iodine with lithium chloride, b) chlorine with lithium bromide?

13) Describe the physical properties of a typical transition metal.

14) Give an industrial use for transition metals.

15) Write down the electron configuration of: a) titanium, b) cobalt, c) zinc.

16) Briefly write down Arrhenius's theory about acids and bases.

17) Why weren't scientists willing to accept the ideas of Arrhenius at first?

18) What is the Brønsted/Lowry definition of an acid? Why were their ideas more readily accepted?

19) What's the difference between a weak acid and a strong acid?

20)* Name a suitable indicator you could use in the titration of potassium hydroxide into ethanoic acid.

21)* In a titration, 49 cm³ of hydrochloric acid was required to neutralise 25 cm³ of sodium hydroxide with a concentration of 0.2 moles per dm³. Calculate the concentration of the hydrochloric acid in: a) mol/dm³   b) g/dm³

22)* Calculate the concentration of the solution formed when 7.5 g of calcium hydroxide, $Ca(OH)_2$, is dissolved in: a) 1 dm³ of water,   b) 100 cm³ of water.

23) Explain why water vapour condenses and falls as rain.

24) Sea water contains dissolved minerals. Where do these come from?

25)* Which of the following will dissolve in water? a) Lead nitrate, b) PbCl, c) ammonium chloride, d) potassium sulfate, e) $AgSO_4$, f) silver chloride, g) $CuSO_4$, h) barium sulfate, i) $Ba(NO_3)_2$.

26) What is a saturated solution?

27)* The graph shows the solubility of lead nitrate in 100 g of water.

a) How much lead nitrate will dissolve in 100 g of water at 40 °C?

b) At what temperature will 70 g of lead nitrate dissolve in 100 g of water?

c) What mass of solid lead nitrate will crystallise when a saturated solution containing 100 g of water is cooled from 60 °C to 40 °C?

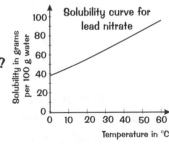

28) Why does a bottle of lemonade fizz up when you open it?

29) What are the main ions that cause water hardness?

30) Give two methods of removing hardness from water.

31) How are microorganisms removed from drinking water?

32) Tap water not pure water. Why don't we make sure that all our drinking water is pure water?

33) Give an example of the social and economic consequences of poor water quality.

Answers on page 76.

Chemistry 3(i) — Elements, Acids and Water

Energy

Whenever chemical reactions occur, there are changes in <u>energy</u>. This is kind of interesting if you think of the number of chemical reactions that are involved in everyday life.

Reactions are <u>Exothermic</u> or Endothermic

See page 34 for more info.

An <u>EXOTHERMIC</u> <u>reaction</u> is one which <u>gives out energy</u> to the surroundings, usually in the form of <u>heat</u> and usually shown by a <u>rise in temperature</u>.

E.g. <u>fuels burning</u> or <u>neutralisation reactions</u>.

An <u>ENDOTHERMIC</u> <u>reaction</u> is one which <u>takes in energy</u> from the surroundings, usually in the form of <u>heat</u> and usually shown by a <u>fall in temperature</u>.

E.g. <u>photosynthesis</u>.

<u>Energy Transfer</u> can be <u>Measured</u>

1) You can measure the amount of <u>energy produced</u> by a <u>chemical reaction</u> (in solution) by taking the <u>temperature of the reagents</u> (making sure they're the same), <u>mixing</u> them in a <u>polystyrene cup</u> and measuring the <u>temperature of the solution</u> at the <u>end</u> of the reaction. Easy.

2) The biggest <u>problem</u> with energy measurements is the amount of energy <u>lost to the surroundings</u>.

3) You can reduce it a bit by putting the polystyrene cup into a <u>beaker of cotton wool</u> to give <u>more insulation</u>, and putting a <u>lid</u> on the cup to reduce energy lost by <u>evaporation</u>.

4) This method works for reactions of <u>solids with water</u> (e.g. dissolving ammonium nitrate in water) as well as with <u>neutralisation</u> reactions.

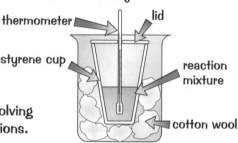

thermometer — lid — polystyrene cup — reaction mixture — cotton wool

Example:
1) Place 25 cm³ of dilute hydrochloric acid in a polystyrene cup, and record the temperature of the acid.
2) Put 25 cm³ of dilute sodium hydroxide in a measuring cylinder and record its temperature.
3) Add the alkali to the acid and stir.
4) Take the temperature of the mixture every 30 seconds, and record the highest temperature it reaches.

<u>Energy Must Always be</u> Supplied <u>to</u> Break bonds...
 ...and Energy is Always <u>Released</u> When <u>Bonds Form</u>

1) During a chemical reaction, <u>old bonds</u> are <u>broken</u> and <u>new bonds</u> are <u>formed</u>.

2) Energy must be <u>supplied</u> to break <u>existing bonds</u> — so bond breaking is an <u>endothermic</u> process. Energy is <u>released</u> when new bonds are <u>formed</u> — so bond formation is an <u>exothermic</u> process.

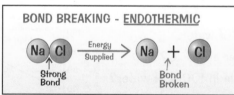

BOND BREAKING - <u>ENDOTHERMIC</u>

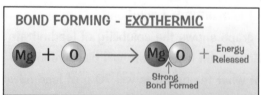

BOND FORMING - <u>EXOTHERMIC</u>

3) In an <u>endothermic</u> reaction, the energy <u>required</u> to break old bonds is <u>greater</u> than the energy <u>released</u> when <u>new bonds</u> are formed.

4) In an <u>exothermic</u> reaction, the energy <u>released</u> in bond formation is <u>greater</u> than the energy used in <u>breaking</u> old bonds.

<u>Save energy — break fewer bonds...</u>

You can get <u>cooling packs</u> that use an <u>endothermic</u> reaction to draw heat from an injury. The pack contains two compartments with different chemicals in. When you use it, you snap the partition and the chemicals <u>mix</u> and <u>react</u>, taking in <u>heat</u> — pretty cool, I reckon (no pun intended).

Energy and Fuels

We burn fuels, and they release energy — so this is an exothermic process.
Just how exothermic you can find by calorimetry. Bet you can't wait...

Fuel Energy is Calculated Using Calorimetry

To measure the amount of energy produced when a fuel is burnt, you can simply burn the fuel and use the flame to heat up some water. Of course, this has to have a fancy chemistry name — calorimetry. Calorimetry uses a metal container, usually made of copper because copper conducts heat so well.

Method:

1) Put 50 g of water in the copper can and record its temperature.
2) Weigh the spirit burner and lid.
3) Put the spirit burner underneath the can, and light the wick. Heat the water, stirring constantly, until the temperature reaches about 50 °C.
4) Put out the flame using the burner lid, and measure the final temperature of the water.
5) Weigh the spirit burner and lid again.

thermometer
lid
copper can
50 cm³ water
draught excluder
spirit burner

*You can use pretty much the same method to calculate the amount of energy produced by foods.
The only problem is that when you set food on fire, it tends to go out after a bit.*

Example: to work out the energy per gram of methylated spirit (meths):

Mass of spirit burner + lid before heating = 68.75 g
Mass of spirit burner + lid after heating = 67.85 g ⟹ Mass of meths burnt = 0.90 g

Temperature of water in copper can before heating = 21.5 °C
Temperature of water in copper can after heating = 52.5 °C ⟹ Temperature rise of 50 g of water due to heating = 31.0 °C

So 0.90 g of fuel produces enough energy to heat up 50 g of water by 31 °C.

It takes 4.2 joules of energy to heat up 1 g of water by 1 °C. ← You'll be told this in the exam.

Therefore, the energy produced in this experiment = 4.2 × 50 × 31 = 6510 joules.

So 0.9 g of meths produces 6510 joules of energy...

... meaning 1 g of meths produces 6510/0.9 = 7233 J or 7.233 kJ ⟸ Energy's wasted heating the can, air, etc — so this figure will often be much lower than the actual energy content.

Different fuels produce different amounts of energy. This table shows some common fuels.

Fuel	Hydrogen	Methane (natural gas)	Butane	Petrol	Meths
Energy (kJ/g)	143	56	50	49	30

Fuels Provide Energy — But There Are Consequences

Fuels release energy which we use in loads of ways — e.g. to generate electricity, to heat our houses, and to power cars, lorries, trains, planes etc. So, hurrah for fuels.

Burning fuels has various effects on the environment. Burning fossil fuels releases CO_2, a greenhouse gas. This causes global warming and climate change. It'll be expensive to slow down these effects, and to put things right. Developing alternative energy sources (e.g. tidal power) costs money.

The price of crude oil has a big economic effect. We use a lot of fuels made from crude oil (e.g. petrol and diesel). When the price of oil goes up, they get more expensive — everything that's transported by lorry, train or plane gets more expensive too. The price of oil is linked to the supply (the less there is, the dearer it gets), and there isn't a bottomless supply of oil. Same goes for natural gas, and coal.

Energy from fuels — it's a burning issue...

Alrighty. A bit of method, a few sums and some social 'n' environmental gubbins to round it off. Fuel never seems so important as when you're running out of it — power cuts and petrol shortages get folk more than a tad ticked off. Crude oil will run out one day for sure, which is a bit of a scary thought.

34

Bond Energies

This is about <u>calculating</u> the stuff that you found by experiment on the previous page.

Energy Level Diagrams _Show if it's_ Exo- _or_ Endo-thermic

In exothermic reactions   ΔH is –ve ← ΔH is the energy change.

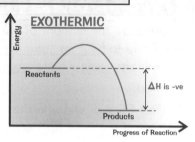

1) This shows an <u>exothermic reaction</u> — the products are at a <u>lower energy</u> than the reactants. The difference in <u>height</u> represents the energy <u>given out</u> in the reaction (per mole). ΔH is –ve here.

2) The <u>initial rise</u> in the line represents the energy needed to <u>break</u> the old bonds. This is the <u>activation energy</u>.

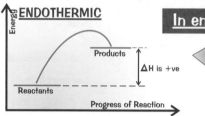

In endothermic reactions   ΔH is +ve

1) This shows an <u>endothermic reaction</u> because the products are at a <u>higher energy</u> than the reactants, so ΔH <u>is +ve</u>.

2) The <u>difference in height</u> represents the <u>energy taken in</u> during the reaction.

The _Activation Energy_ is _Lowered_ by _Catalysts_

See your Chemistry 2 notes for more about catalysts.

1) The <u>activation energy</u> represents the <u>minimum energy</u> needed by reacting particles for the reaction to occur.

2) A <u>catalyst</u> makes reactions happen <u>easier</u> (and therefore quicker) by <u>reducing</u> the initial energy needed.

3) This is represented by the <u>lower curve</u> on the diagram showing a <u>lower activation energy</u>.

4) The <u>overall energy change</u> for the reaction, ΔH, <u>remains the same</u> though.

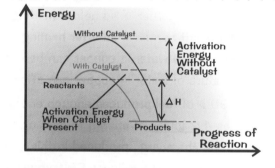

Bond Energy Calculations — _Need to be Practised_

1) <u>Every</u> chemical bond has a particular <u>bond energy</u> associated with it. This <u>bond energy</u> varies slightly depending what <u>compound</u> the bond occurs in — don't worry you'll be given the ones you need to use.

2) You can use these <u>known bond energies</u> to calculate the <u>overall energy change</u> for a reaction. You need to <u>practise</u> a few of these, but the basic idea is really very simple...

Example: The Formation of HCl

Using known bond energies you can <u>calculate</u> the <u>energy change</u> for this reaction: ➤ $H_2 + Cl_2 \rightarrow 2HCl$

The bond energies you need are: H—H: +436 kJ/mol; Cl—Cl: +242 kJ/mol; H—Cl: +431 kJ/mol.

1) <u>Breaking</u> one mole of H—H and one mole of Cl—Cl bonds <u>requires</u> 436 + 242 = <u>+678 kJ</u>

2) <u>Forming</u> <u>two</u> moles of H—Cl bonds <u>releases</u> 2 × 431 = <u>862 kJ</u>

3) <u>Overall</u> more energy is <u>released</u> than is used to form the products: 862 – 678 = <u>184 kJ/mol</u> released.

4) Since this is energy <u>released</u>, if we wanted to show ΔH we'd need to put a <u>negative sign</u> in front of it to indicate that it's an <u>exothermic</u> reaction, like this: ΔH = –184 kJ/mol

Energy transfer — _make sure you take it all in..._

I admit — it's a bit like maths, this. But think how many times you've heard <u>energy efficiency</u> mentioned over the last few years. Well, this kind of calculation is used in working out whether we're using resources efficiently or not. So even if it's not exciting, it's useful at least.

Chemistry 3(ii) — Energy and Chemical Tests

Energy and Food

You (and me as well, I'm told) are just a mass of <u>chemical reactions</u>. You take in fuel (food), and convert the energy it contains. That's what you do. Among other things.

Food Energy is Often Measured in calories and Kilocalories

1) Back on page 33, the calorimetry calculation for the amount of energy in a fuel gives the answer in <u>joules</u>. The <u>joule</u> is the <u>standard unit of energy</u> used by all scientists, and it replaced an older unit of energy called the <u>calorie</u>.

> 1 calorie = <u>amount of energy</u> needed to raise the temp of <u>1 g of water</u> by <u>1 °C</u>. 1 calorie = <u>4.2 joules</u>.

2) The dietary information on food labels is in <u>kilocalories</u> (kilo- means 1000, remember). Confusingly, on food labels they don't usually write it as "kilocalorie" or "kcal". That would be far too straightforward. They usually write it as <u>Calorie</u>, with a capital C.

> 1 <u>Calorie</u> (big-C) = amount of energy needed to raise the temp of <u>1 KILOGRAM of water</u> by 1 °C.
> 1 <u>Calorie</u> = <u>4200 joules</u>.

And even when the food manufacturers write small-C calories on the food label, they really mean big-C calories. Kilocalories. ARGH!

You Get Your Energy from Food

As with all fuels, different foods produce <u>different amounts of energy</u>.

1) The composition of the food determines how much energy it produces. Foods with high proportions of <u>fats</u> and <u>oils</u> produce relatively <u>large amounts of energy</u>.

2) <u>Carbohydrates</u> produce <u>some</u> energy, but much less than fats and oils.

3) <u>Proteins</u> contain about as much energy as carbohydrates, but we don't tend to use it for energy in our bodies.

4) The <u>table</u> on the right shows the difference in energy content between a <u>chocolate bar</u> and a <u>chicken breast</u>.

	Chocolate (per 100 g)	Chicken breast (per 100 g)
Energy	525 kcal	164 kcal
Protein	7.6 g	27 g
Carbohydrate	56.1 g	–
Fat	30.1 g	6.2 g
Sodium	–	0.3 g

Taking in More Fuel Than You Use Means the Excess is Stored

1) Your body needs energy to perform all your <u>daily activities</u> — including tasks you do without thinking, e.g. breathing, heart beating etc. Chemical reactions in your cells that go on <u>all the time</u> need energy.

2) The energy in food is <u>released</u> by the process of <u>respiration</u>, where glucose reacts with oxygen to produce carbon dioxide, water and energy. This goes on in your cells <u>all the time</u>.

> glucose + oxygen $\rightarrow$ carbon dioxide + water + ENERGY

3) When the food you eat contains <u>more energy</u> than your body needs, the excess food gets <u>stored</u> by the body as <u>fat</u>. Continually taking on more energy than you need will eventually make you <u>obese</u>.

4) When the food you eat contains <u>less energy</u> than your body needs, your body <u>uses up</u> some of its <u>fat stores</u>. <u>Calorie-controlled diets</u> are designed to give the body <u>slightly less energy</u> than it needs each day, e.g. a person who uses up 2000 kcal a day could eat 1700 kcal a day and gradually lose fat.

5) Most calorie-controlled diets are <u>low fat</u> diets. Calorie-controlled diets usually avoid <u>sugar</u>, because it's high in energy and it <u>stimulates the appetite</u>. Some weight loss diets recommend "<u>slow release</u>" carbohydrates such as wholemeal bread and oats because they <u>fill you up for longer</u> than white bread or sugary carbohydrates, making you <u>less likely</u> to scoff <u>snacks</u> between meals.

All very "fashion and lifestyle" if you ask me...

Weight loss is nothing more than energy in/energy out at the end of the day, so there are two ways to go at it — <u>eat less energy-rich food</u>, or <u>do more exercise</u> to use up more energy. Or (gasp) do <u>both</u>. Learn which types of food are energy rich, and don't forget that calories and Calories are different.

Tests for Cations

Forensic science involves a lot of chemical tests, which is what these next pages are about.
Before you start reading, you have to pretend you have a mystery substance. You don't know what it is, but you need to find out — just like that bloke off the telly who investigates murders.

First off, some tests for cations (positive ions — such as Na^+ or Ca^{2+}).

Flame Tests Identify Metal Ions

Compounds of some metals burn with a characteristic colour (as you see every November 5th).

So you can test for various metal ions by heating your substance
and seeing whether it burns with a distinctive colour flame.

- Lithium, Li^+, burns with a crimson-red flame.
- Sodium, Na^+, burns with an yellow-orange flame.
- Potassium, K^+, burns with a lilac flame.
- Calcium, Ca^{2+}, burns with a brick-red flame.
- Barium, Ba^{2+}, burns with a green flame.

Some Metals Form a Coloured Precipitate with NaOH

This is also a test for metal ions, but it's slightly more involved. Concentrate now...

1) Many metal hydroxides are insoluble and precipitate out of solution when formed.
   Some of these hydroxides have a characteristic colour.

2) So in this test you add a few drops of sodium hydroxide solution to a solution of your mystery
   compound — all in the hope of forming an insoluble hydroxide.

3) If you get a coloured insoluble hydroxide you can then tell which metal was in the compound.

"Metal"	Colour of precipitate	Ionic Reaction
Calcium, Ca^{2+}	White	$Ca^{2+}(aq) + 2OH^-(aq) \rightarrow Ca(OH)_2(s)$
Copper(II), Cu^{2+}	Blue	$Cu^{2+}(aq) + 2OH^-(aq) \rightarrow Cu(OH)_2(s)$
Iron(II), Fe^{2+}	Sludgy green	$Fe^{2+}(aq) + 2OH^-(aq) \rightarrow Fe(OH)_2(s)$
Iron(III), Fe^{3+}	Reddish brown	$Fe^{3+}(aq) + 3OH^-(aq) \rightarrow Fe(OH)_3(s)$
Aluminium, Al^{3+}	White at first. But then redissolves in excess NaOH to form a colourless solution.	$Al^{3+}(aq) + 3OH^-(aq) \rightarrow Al(OH)_3(s)$ then $Al(OH)_3(s) + OH^-(aq) \rightarrow Al(OH)_4^-(aq)$
Magnesium, Mg^{2+}	White	$Mg^{2+}(aq) + 2OH^-(aq) \rightarrow Mg(OH)_2(s)$

"Ammonium Compound + NaOH" Gives Off (Stinky) Ammonia

1) Ammonia (NH_3) is smelly — it reeks of cat wee. This is a good way
   to tell if there's ammonia about, usually — the smell's quite distinctive.

   Tip: waft the smell towards your nose. Don't take big snorts — ammonia's a bit poisonous.

2) Another way is to use damp red litmus paper — ammonia turns it blue.

3) You can use this fact to test for ammonium ions (NH_4^+) using sodium hydroxide.
   Add sodium hydroxide to a solution of your mystery substance — ammonia given off means
   there are ammonium ions in your mystery substance. No nasty ammonia smell means no NH_4^+.

The Ammonia Mystery — smells like my cat did it...

Remember... your cation is your metal ion, and cations are positive — they'd be attracted to a cathode
(which is negative, remember). Now these tests assume that your mystery substance is ionic, which of
course it might not be. But you might be able to tell — ionic substances tend to be crystalline solids
with a high melting point. So, if it's a gas, a volatile liquid (you might be able to smell it) or a soft solid,
no need to bother with these tests. See p.38 for how to test for organic (carbon-chain) compounds.

Tests for Anions

So now maybe you know what the <u>positive</u> part of your mystery substance is.
Now it's time to test for the <u>negative</u> bit — or <u>anion</u>.

Testing for Carbonates — Check for CO$_2$

First thing's first — the test for carbon dioxide (CO_2).

1) You can test to see if a gas is <u>carbon dioxide</u> by bubbling it through <u>limewater</u>. If it is <u>carbon dioxide</u>, the <u>limewater turns milky</u>:

2) You can use this to test for <u>carbonates</u>, since carbonates react with <u>dilute acids</u> to form <u>carbon dioxide</u>.

> Acid + Carbonate → Salt + Water + Carbon dioxide

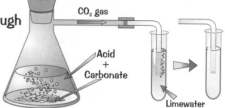

And Some Carbonates Change Colour When They Decompose

Sometimes, a <u>colour change</u> during a reaction can give you clues to the identity of a substance.

1) Method: put one spatula of carbonate into an <u>test tube</u> and heat strongly, then allow to cool.

2) <u>Copper carbonate</u> turns from <u>green</u> to black and it stays black when cool.

> $CuCO_3$(s, green) $\longrightarrow$ CuO(s, black) + CO_2(g)

3) <u>Zinc carbonate</u> turns from white to <u>yellow</u>, but when it cools down it turns back to white.

> $ZnCO_3$(s, white) $\longrightarrow$ ZnO(s, yellow when hot, white when cold) + CO_2(g)

Test for Sulfates (SO$_4{}^{2-}$) and Halides (Cl$^-$, Br$^-$, I$^-$)

You can test for certain ions by seeing if a <u>precipitate</u> is formed after these reactions...

Sulfate Ions, SO$_4{}^{2-}$

1) To test for a <u>sulfate</u> ion ($SO_4{}^{2-}$), <u>add dilute HCl</u>, followed by <u>barium chloride solution</u>, $BaCl_2$.

2) A <u>white</u> precipitate of <u>barium sulfate</u> means the original compound was a sulfate.

$$Ba^{2+}(aq) + SO_4{}^{2-}(aq) \longrightarrow BaSO_4(s)$$

Chloride, Bromide or Iodide Ions, Cl$^-$, Br$^-$, I$^-$

To test for <u>chloride</u>, <u>bromide</u> or <u>iodide</u> ions, add <u>dilute nitric acid</u> (HNO_3), followed by <u>silver nitrate solution</u> ($AgNO_3$).

A <u>chloride</u> gives a **white** precipitate of <u>silver chloride</u>. $Ag^+(aq) + Cl^-(aq) \longrightarrow AgCl(s)$
A <u>bromide</u> gives a **cream** precipitate of <u>silver bromide</u>. $Ag^+(aq) + Br^-(aq) \longrightarrow AgBr(s)$
An <u>iodide</u> gives a **yellow** precipitate of <u>silver iodide</u>. $Ag^+(aq) + I^-(aq) \longrightarrow AgI(s)$

The Test for Nitrates (NO$_3{}^-$) Produces Ammonia

1) Mix some of your mystery compound with a little <u>aluminium powder</u>.

2) Then add a few drops of <u>sodium hydroxide</u> solution and heat.
   If you started off with a nitrate, it'll be reduced to <u>ammonia</u>.

3) As always, test for ammonia using your <u>nose</u> or, better, damp <u>red</u> litmus paper (which will turn <u>blue</u>).

Don't just guess that your substance contains any old anion...

So you might have to do loads of different chemical tests to find out all the information about your mystery substance. It's a bit like detective work — eliminating suspects, narrowing down possibilities, and so on. It's the kind of stuff <u>exam questions</u> are made of, by the way, so be warned. They might give you the <u>results</u> from several chemical tests, and you have to say what the substance is. See p.40.

Tests for Organic Compounds

The previous pages were about testing <u>inorganic</u> compounds (things not built around a chain of carbon atoms). But your mystery substance might just as easily be <u>organic</u>. In that case, here's what you do...

Organic Compounds Burn When Heated

1) Organic compounds burn in air, with a <u>yellowy-orange and/or blue flame</u>. The greater the proportion of carbon in the compound, the more <u>yellow</u> and smoky the flame is.

2) When there's <u>plenty of air</u> available, burning a hydrocarbon produces <u>carbon dioxide</u> and <u>water</u>. If the amount of air is reduced, then <u>carbon monoxide</u> (a poisonous gas), and <u>carbon</u> (soot) can also be produced.

A hydrocarbon is an organic compound containing only carbon and hydrogen, remember.

3) <u>Solid</u> organic compounds will <u>char</u> — i.e. their surface will get <u>scorched with black marks</u> of <u>carbon</u>.

Compounds with C=C Bonds Decolourise Bromine Water

The test for C=C double bonds is a <u>piece of cake</u> (though not literally).

1) If your organic compound is <u>unsaturated</u> (i.e. it has <u>double</u> or <u>triple</u> bonds between carbon atoms), it'll <u>decolourise bromine water</u>.

2) If your organic compound is <u>saturated</u> (i.e. there are <u>no</u> double or triple bonds), the bromine water will stay <u>brown</u>.

3) You can do this test on <u>margarine</u>, which has C=C bonds. Shake 1 cm³ of bromine water with a small amount of <u>melted margarine</u>, and the bromine water decolourises.

...so this one's unsaturated.

Find the Empirical Formula of an Organic Compound by Burning It

An empirical formula shows the ratios of all the elements in a substance.

It's possible to work out the empirical formula of an organic compound by burning a <u>known mass</u> of it completely in <u>oxygen</u>, and measuring the <u>masses</u> of all the <u>products</u>.

With a hydrocarbon, all the carbon ends up in CO_2 and all the hydrogen ends up in water. So...

Step 1) Find the <u>mass of each element</u> in the compound.
- To find the mass of <u>carbon</u> in the compound, multiply the mass of CO_2 produced by the proportion of C in CO_2.
- To find the mass of <u>hydrogen</u> in the compound, multiply the mass of H_2O produced by the proportion of H in H_2O.

Using relative atomic masses, the proportion of C in CO_2 is $12 \div 44 = 0.2727...$

And the proportion of H in H_2O is $2 \div 18 = 0.1111...$

Step 2) Divide these masses of C and H by the <u>atomic masses</u> of C and H (to find the number of <u>moles</u>).

Step 3) Divide both answers by the <u>smallest one</u>. This gives the <u>simplest ratio</u> of atoms of each element.

<u>Example:</u> 0.4 g of an organic hydrocarbon is burnt completely in oxygen. 1.1 g of carbon dioxide and 0.9 g of water are formed. What is the compound's <u>empirical formula</u>?

Step 1 — Find the mass of carbon in the compound: $1.1 \times (12 \div 44) = \underline{0.3\ g}$
Do the same for hydrogen: $0.9 \times (2 \div 18) = \underline{0.1\ g}$

Step 2 — The relative atomic mass of carbon is 12, so: $0.3 \div 12 = \underline{0.025\ mol}$
The relative atomic mass of hydrogen is 1, so: $0.1 \div 1 = \underline{0.1\ mol}$

Step 3 — Divide the biggest answer by the smallest one to get the ratio of carbon to hydrogen. The simplest whole number ratio of atoms of each element is $0.1 \div 0.025 = \underline{4}$ (meaning there is 1 carbon to 4 hydrogens). This gives an empirical formula for this compound of $\underline{CH_4}$.

How many of these formula doodahs can one substance need...

Finding an empirical formula involves an awful lot of sums. Sure, they're simple sums taken one by one, but it'd be all too easy to get confused, do them in the <u>wrong order</u>, and end up with completely the wrong answer. Learn the three steps and follow them — <u>mass</u>, then <u>moles</u>, then <u>ratio</u>.

Instrumental Methods

Nowadays you can turn to <u>machines</u> to do the donkey work of identifying substances, if need be.

Machines Can Also Analyse Unknown Substances

1) Machines are useful for <u>medical</u> purposes, police <u>forensic</u> work, <u>environmental</u> analysis, checking whether an athlete has taken a <u>banned</u> substance, analysis of products in <u>industry</u>, and so on.

2) Rapid advances in <u>electronics</u> and <u>computing</u> have made more advanced analysis possible.

<u>Advantages of Using Machines</u>
- Can be operated by <u>technicians</u>. Lab methods need <u>trained chemists</u> to do everything.
- <u>More accurate</u> than lab methods, and can detect even the <u>tiniest amounts</u> of substances.
- <u>Much faster</u> than lab methods, and tests can be automated.

<u>Disadvantages of Using Machines</u>
- It's <u>very expensive</u> to buy, run and maintain the machines.

'Lab methods' means doing tests like the ones on pages 36-38.

Atomic Absorption Spectroscopy Identifies Metals

1) Atomic absorption spectroscopy is a little bit like a flame test machine, and is used for identifying <u>metals</u>.

2) The patterns of light <u>absorbed</u> by the metals in the sample are analysed. Each metal present in the sample produces a <u>different</u> pattern.

3) It's much <u>faster</u> and much more <u>reliable</u> than can be done with the human eye.

4) The <u>steel industry</u> uses atomic absorption spectroscopy to check the composition of the steels it produces. (Each kind of steel has to have the right composition to make it suitable for its particular use.) This only takes <u>minutes</u>, compared to days with the lab method.

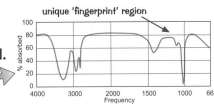
beep beep... vrrrr... definitely sodium

Other Techniques Identify Elements or Compounds

① **Infrared (IR) Spectrometry**

This technique identifies which frequencies of <u>infrared</u> radiation are absorbed — the <u>pattern</u> of absorbance is <u>unique</u> for every compound. This '<u>fingerprint</u>' allows identification of individual compounds.

unique 'fingerprint' region

% absorbed — 100, 80, 60, 40, 20, 0
Frequency — 4000, 3000, 2000, 1500, 1000, 668

② **Ultraviolet (UV) Spectroscopy**

Similar to infrared spectroscopy, but with <u>ultraviolet light</u>.

③ **Nuclear Magnetic Resonance (NMR) Spectroscopy**

This method is used for <u>organic compounds</u>. It shows what atoms the hydrogen atoms are connected to. This helps find the structure of the molecule, by telling you if there are -OH groups, $-NH_2$ groups etc.

④ **Gas-Liquid Chromatography**

This uses a similar principle to paper chromatography. It's used to identify <u>gases and liquids</u>.

⑤ **Mass Spectrometry**

This method can be used for <u>both elements and compounds</u>. It tells you the <u>mass</u> of each molecule/particle. For elements, this tells you exactly what element you've got, and for larger molecules the mass is a good clue.

Unfortunately, machines can't do the exam for you...

Luckily, you <u>aren't</u> expected to know the details of how these machines work. What you <u>do need to know</u> is: what each one tells you, and what kind of substances they're used for (gases, liquids, elements, etc). Plus, be sure to learn the <u>advantages and disadvantages</u> of machine analysis.

Identifying Unknown Substances

In the <u>exam</u>, you might have to <u>apply</u> your knowledge, which is kind of scary. It means <u>thinking</u>. Eeek.
Most likely, you'll have to <u>interpret information</u> that the examiners provide. Just keep your head.

Using Chemical Tests

Time for a <u>walk-through</u> of a <u>typical question</u> that could come up in the exam. It uses the identification
tests from pages 36-37 — if you don't know those thoroughly, <u>go back and learn 'em</u>.

Compound A is a <u>bluey-green crystalline solid</u> that dissolves in water to give a <u>blue solution</u>.
A <u>flame test</u> was carried out on compound A, and a <u>bright green colour</u> was produced.
The following tests were then carried out on separate samples of the solution of compound A,
and the results for each test are recorded in the table. From the information given, identify compound A.

1) Add a few drops of sodium hydroxide	A blue precipitate is formed
2) Add 5 cm³ of hydrochloric acid	No change
3) Add 2 cm³ dilute hydrochloric acid followed by 2 cm³ of barium chloride	No change
4) Add a little aluminium powder, a few drops of sodium hydroxide solution and warm.	A blue precipitate is formed, but no bubbles of gas.
5) Add 2 cm³ dilute nitric acid followed by 2 cm³ of silver nitrate	A white precipitate is formed

OK, it's a <u>crystalline solid</u>, so it's <u>ionic</u>. You can identify it in two parts — first identify the <u>cation</u>
by looking at the tests that tell you something about the cation, then do the same for the <u>anion</u>.

Cation: The <u>flame test</u> result tells you the cation <u>can't</u> be lithium, sodium, potassium, calcium or barium.
Test 1 shows that it's <u>copper</u>, because there's a <u>blue precipitate</u> of <u>copper hydroxide</u>.

Anion: Test 2 indicates it's <u>not a carbonate</u> because there were <u>no bubbles of gas</u>.
Test 3 shows it's <u>not a sulfate</u> — there's <u>no white precipitate</u>.
Test 4 is the test for <u>nitrates</u> — <u>no ammonia</u> means <u>no nitrate</u>. (The blue precipitate is formed
because NaOH has been added to a solution of copper ions — like in Test 1.)
Test 5 tells you that a <u>chloride ion</u> is there because of the <u>white precipitate</u> of silver chloride.

Compound A is therefore <u>COPPER CHLORIDE</u>.

Using Instrumental Analysis

Or you might have to interpret results from an <u>instrumental analysis</u>...

A local health authority received reports that some bottles of wine were <u>contaminated</u>.
Scientists isolated a compound from the wine and analysed the substance using <u>IR</u> and
<u>mass spectrometry</u>. The IR spectrum is as shown:

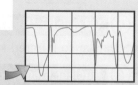

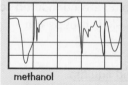

methanol

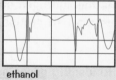

ethanol

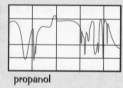

propanol

A forensic scientist compared the IR spectrum
of the unknown with IR spectra of
<u>methanol (CH₃OH)</u>, <u>ethanol (C₂H₅OH)</u>
and <u>propanol (C₃H₇OH)</u> (on the left).
What conclusions could the scientist draw?

The scientist could say the substance <u>isn't propanol</u> because the IR spectra are very different.
(Those for methanol and ethanol are similar, so it's tricky to decide between these — more evidence would be good.)

The mass spectrum showed that the relative molecular mass (M_r) of the unknown compound was 32.

The M_r of methanol (CH_3OH) is $(1 \times 12) + (4 \times 1) + (1 \times 16) = 32$, and the M_r of ethanol (C_2H_5OH)
is $(2 \times 12) + (6 \times 1) + (1 \times 16) = 46$. So the contamination was due to <u>METHANOL</u>.

If you aren't part of the solution, you're part of the precipitate...

In the exam they may well give you the results of a bunch of tests and ask you to identify a substance.
So learning one or two tests might not help much — you <u>need them all</u>, see.

Revision Summary for Chemistry 3(ii)

Whenever anything at all happens, energy is either taken in or released. So it's amazingly important. If that doesn't inspire you to learn the stuff about it, the fact that you're likely to get exam questions on it should. There are bag loads of chemical tests in this section too. There's no easy way to remember them — you just have to do some good old-fashioned memorising. Anyway, enough words of wisdom, try these questions:

1) An acid and an alkali were mixed in a polystyrene cup, as shown below. The acid and alkali were each at 20 °C before they were mixed. After they were mixed, the temperature of the solution reached 24 °C.

   a) State whether this reaction is exothermic or endothermic.

   b) Explain why the cotton wool is used.

2) Is energy released when bonds are formed or when bonds are broken?

3) The apparatus on the right is used to measure how much energy is released when pentane is burnt. It takes 4.2 joules of energy to heat 1 g of water by 1 °C.

   *a) Using the following data, calculate the amount of energy per gram of pentane.

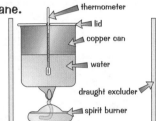

Mass of empty copper can	64 g	Initial temperature of water	17 °C
Mass of copper can + water	116 g	Final temperature of water	47 °C

Mass of sprit burner + pentane before burning	97.72 g
Mass of sprit burner + pentane after burning	97.37 g

   b) A data book says that pentane has 49 kJ/g of energy. Why is the amount you calculated different?

4) Explain why the price of bananas might rise if we keep burning so much fuel.

5) a) Draw energy level diagrams for exothermic and endothermic reactions.

   b) Explain how bond breaking and forming relate to these diagrams.

6) What is the activation energy for a reaction? Mark it on your exothermic energy level diagram from Q5.

7) How does a catalyst affect: a) activation energy, b) overall energy change for a reaction?

8) *a) Calculate the energy change for the following reaction: $2H_2 + O_2 \rightarrow 2H_2O$

   You need these bond energies: H–H: +436 kJ/mol, O=O: +496 kJ/mol, O–H: +463 kJ/mol

   Hint: There are 2 O–H bonds in each molecule of water.

   *b) Is this an exothermic or endothermic reaction?

9)* A tin of beans contains 655 kJ of energy. How many calories does it contain? How many kcal is this?

10) Give a reason why your body uses energy all the time, not just when you exercise.

11) What happens if the food you eat contains more energy than you need?

12) Explain how you can test for the following ions. Give ionic equations where appropriate.
    a) Li^+, b) K^+, c) Ba^{2+}, d) Ca^{2+}, e) Fe^{2+}, f) Al^{3+}, g) NH_4^+, h) SO_4^{2-}, i) Cl^-, j) I^-, k) NO_3^-

13) How would you distinguish between solutions of: a) magnesium sulfate and aluminium sulfate, b) sodium bromide and sodium iodide, c) copper nitrate and copper sulfate?

14) Describe what you would notice when you heated: a) copper carbonate, b) zinc carbonate. What is produced when these compounds react with a dilute acid?

15) Explain how you could distinguish between butane and butene.

16) What's an empirical formula?

17)* An organic hydrocarbon is burnt completely in oxygen. 4.4 g of carbon dioxide and 1.8 g of water are formed. What is the compound's empirical formula?

18) Give three advantages of instrumental analysis over traditional lab methods.

19) What lab test is atomic emission spectroscopy a bit like? Why does the steel industry use it?

20) What kind of information does NMR spectroscopy give you about an unknown substance?

* Answers on page 76.

Chemistry 3(ii) — Energy and Chemical Tests

Turning Forces and Centre of Mass

No time to waste — let's get straight in with <u>turning forces</u>. Not very difficult... not very exciting either.
Expect to be royally sick of pivots and centre of mass by the time you've finished these pages.

A *Moment* is the *Turning Effect* of a Force

MOMENT (Nm) = FORCE (N) × perpendicular DISTANCE (m) between line of action and pivot

1) The <u>force</u> on the spanner causes a <u>turning effect</u>
   or <u>moment</u> on the nut. A <u>larger</u> force would
   mean a <u>larger</u> moment.

   Tough nut

   Force = 10 N   Distance = 0.1 m

   Moment = 10 × 0.1
   = <u>1 Nm</u>

2) Using a longer spanner, the same force can
   exert a <u>larger</u> moment because the <u>distance</u>
   from the pivot is <u>greater</u>.

   10 N   0.2 m   Pivot

   Moment = 10 × 0.2
   = <u>2 Nm</u>

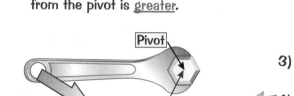

Pivot

Force

Perpendicular
distance

3) To get the <u>maximum</u> moment (or turning effect) you need
   to push at <u>right angles</u> (<u>perpendicular</u>) to the spanner.

4) Pushing at <u>any other angle</u> means a smaller moment
   because the <u>perpendicular</u> distance between
   the line of action and the pivot is <u>smaller</u>.

The Centre of Mass Hangs *Directly Below* the *Point of Suspension*

1) You can think of the <u>centre of mass</u> of an object as the point at which the <u>whole</u> mass is concentrated.

2) A freely suspended object will <u>swing</u> until its centre of mass is <u>vertically below</u> the <u>point of suspension</u>.

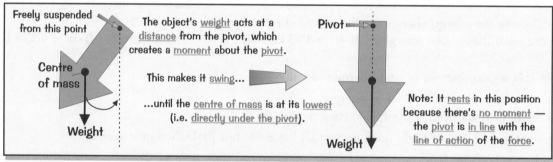

Freely suspended
from this point

Centre
of mass

Weight

The object's <u>weight</u> acts at a
<u>distance</u> from the pivot, which
creates a <u>moment</u> about the <u>pivot</u>.

This makes it <u>swing</u>...

...until the <u>centre of mass</u> is at its <u>lowest</u>
(i.e. <u>directly under the pivot</u>).

Pivot

Weight

Note: It <u>rests</u> in this position
because there's <u>no moment</u> —
the <u>pivot</u> is <u>in line</u> with the
<u>line of action</u> of the <u>force</u>.

3) This means you can find the <u>centre of mass</u> of any flat shape like this:

   1) Suspend the shape and a <u>plumb line</u> from the
      same point, and wait until they <u>stop moving</u>.
   2) <u>Draw</u> a line along the plumb line.
   3) Do the same thing again, but suspend the shape
      from a <u>different</u> pivot point.
   4) The centre of mass is where your two lines <u>cross</u>.

   Pivot

   Picture of
   snowman.

   Centre
   of mass

   Plumb line

4) But you don't need to go to all that trouble for <u>simple</u> shapes.
   You can quickly guess where the centre of
   mass is by looking for <u>lines of symmetry</u>.

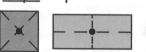 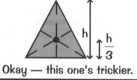

$\frac{h}{3}$ h

Okay — this one's trickier.

Be at the centre of mass — sit on the middle pew...

Think of the extra force you need to open a door by pushing it <u>near the hinge</u> compared to <u>at the handle</u>
— the <u>distance from pivot</u> is <u>less</u>, so you need <u>more force</u> to get the <u>same moment</u>. Best way to
understand it is to do <u>loads of practice</u>. Get your teacher to give you some extra moment questions.

Balanced Moments and Stability

Once you can calculate moments, you can work out if a <u>seesaw is balanced</u>. Useful thing, Physics.

A Question of Balance — Are the Moments Equal?

If the <u>anticlockwise moments</u> are equal to the <u>clockwise moments</u>, the object <u>won't turn</u>.

Example 1: Your younger brother weighs <u>300 N</u> and sits <u>2 m</u> from the <u>pivot</u> of a seesaw.
If you weigh <u>700 N</u>, where should you sit to <u>balance</u> the seesaw?

For the seesaw to <u>balance</u>:

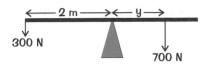

Total Anticlockwise Moments = Total Clockwise Moments

anticlockwise moment = clockwise moment
$$300 \times 2 = 700 \times y$$
$$y = \underline{0.86 \text{ m}}$$

Ignore the weight of the seesaw — its centre of mass is on the pivot, so it doesn't have a turning effect.

Example 2: A <u>6 m</u> long steel girder weighing <u>1000 N</u> rests horizontally on a pole <u>1 m</u> from one end.
What is the <u>tension</u> in a supporting cable attached vertically to the other end?

The '<u>tension in the cable</u>' bit makes it sound harder than it actually is.
But the girder's <u>weight</u> is <u>balanced</u> by the tension <u>force</u> in the cable, so...

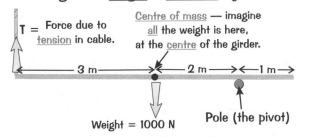

T = Force due to <u>tension</u> in cable.

<u>Centre of mass</u> — imagine <u>all</u> the weight is here, at the <u>centre</u> of the girder.

Weight = 1000 N

Pole (the pivot)

anticlockwise moment (due to weight) = clockwise moment (due to tension in cable)
$$1000 \times 2 = T \times 5$$
$$2000 = 5T$$
and so $\underline{T = 400 \text{ N}}$

And if they're Not Equal...

If the Total Anticlockwise Moments do not equal the Total Clockwise Moments, there will be a Resultant Moment	...so the object will turn.

Low and Wide Objects are Most Stable

<u>Unstable</u> objects tip over easily — <u>stable</u> ones don't. The position of the centre of mass is <u>all-important</u>.

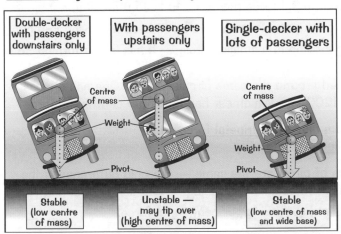

Double-decker with passengers downstairs only

With passengers upstairs only

Single-decker with lots of passengers

Centre of mass

Weight

Pivot

Centre of mass

Weight

Pivot

Stable (low centre of mass)

Unstable — may tip over (high centre of mass)

Stable (low centre of mass and wide base)

1) The most <u>stable</u> objects have a <u>wide base</u> and a <u>low centre of mass</u>.

2) An object will begin to <u>tip over</u> if its centre of mass moves <u>beyond</u> the edge of its base.

3) Again it's because of <u>moments</u> — if the weight <u>doesn't</u> act <u>in line</u> with the <u>pivot</u>, it'll cause a <u>resultant moment</u>. This will either right the object or tip it over.

Centre of mass

Edge of base

Balanced moments — nope, not had one of those for a while...

Any time you've got two <u>equal and opposite moments</u>, you've got <u>equilibrium</u>, and your thing-on-a-pivot will stay still. Remember that and you won't go far wrong (as long as you calculate moments properly). <u>Learn</u> the factors that make an object hard to tip over — a <u>low centre of mass</u> and a <u>good wide base</u>.

Circular Motion

If it wasn't for <u>circular</u> motion our little planet would just be wandering aimlessly around the Universe. And as soon as you launched a <u>satellite</u>, it'd just go flying off into space. Hardly ideal.

Circular Motion — *Velocity* is *Constantly Changing*

1) Velocity is both the speed and direction of an object.
2) If an object is travelling in a circle it is <u>constantly changing direction</u>, which means it's <u>accelerating</u>.
3) This means there <u>must</u> be a <u>force</u> acting on it.
4) This force acts towards the centre of the circle.
5) This force that keeps something moving in a circle is called a <u>centripetal force</u>.

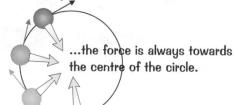

The velocity's in this direction, but...

...the force is always towards the centre of the circle.

Pronounced sen-tree-pee-tal

In the exam, you can be asked to say <u>which force</u> is actually providing the centripetal force in a given situation. It can be <u>tension</u>, or <u>friction</u>, or even <u>gravity</u> (see next page).

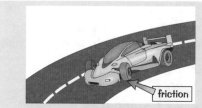

<u>A car going round a bend</u>:
1) Imagine the bend is part of a <u>circle</u> — the centripetal force is towards the <u>centre</u> of the circle.
2) The force is from <u>friction</u> between the car's tyres and the road.

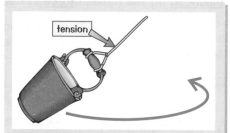

<u>A bucket whirling round on a rope</u>:
The centripetal force comes from <u>tension in the rope</u>. Break the rope, and the bucket flies off at a tangent.

<u>A spinning fairground ride</u>:
The centripetal force comes from <u>tension</u> in the <u>spokes of the ride</u>.

Centripetal Force depends on *Mass, Speed* and *Radius*

1) The <u>faster</u> an object's moving, the <u>bigger</u> the centripetal force has to be to keep it moving in a <u>circle</u>.
2) Likewise, the <u>heavier</u> the object, the <u>bigger</u> the centripetal force has to be to keep it moving in a <u>circle</u>.
3) And you need a <u>larger force</u> to keep something moving in a <u>smaller circle</u> — it has 'more turning' to do.

Example: Two cars are driving at the same speed around the same circular track. One has a mass of 900 kg, the other has a mass of 1200 kg. Which car has the larger centripetal force?

The <u>three things</u> that mean you need a <u>bigger centripetal force</u> are: <u>more speed</u>, <u>more mass</u>, <u>smaller radius</u> of circle.

In this example, the speed and radius of circle are the same — the <u>only difference</u> is the <u>masses</u> of the cars. So you don't need to calculate anything — you can confidently say: The <u>1200 kg car</u> (the heavier one) must have the <u>larger centripetal force</u>.

Circular motion — get round to learning it...

To understand this, you need to learn that <u>constant change in direction means constant acceleration</u>. Velocity is a vector — it has direction, and acceleration is change in velocity. When there's acceleration, there's force (see, easy). Learn what forces can provide centripetal force — tension, friction etc.

Gravity and Planetary Orbits

Gravity is not just important for keeping us all stuck to the ground — it's also the force that keeps the Moon and satellites orbiting round the Earth, and planets orbiting round stars...

Gravity is the Centripetal Force that Keeps Planets in Orbit

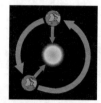

1) Gravity is the force of attraction between masses — the larger the masses the greater the force of gravity between them (you're strongly attracted to a big mass like the Earth, but not to a small mass like a toaster).

2) This gravitational force can act as the centripetal force that keeps one object moving in a circular path (orbit) round another. An orbit is possible when there's a balance between the forward motion of the object and the gravitational force pulling it inwards.
(If there wasn't a balance, the smaller object would either get pulled inwards or fly off at a tangent.)

3) Planets always orbit around stars. E.g. the Earth orbits around the Sun, and the centripetal force needed is provided by the gravitational attraction between the Earth and the Sun.
(And likewise all the other planets in the Solar System of course.)

4) These orbits are all slightly elliptical (elongated circles) with the Sun at one focus of the ellipse.

5) The further the planet is from the Sun, the longer its orbit takes (see below).

Gravity Decreases Quickly as You Get Further Away

1) With very large masses like stars and planets, gravity is very big and is felt a long way out.

2) The closer you get to a star or a planet, the stronger the force of attraction.

3) To counteract the stronger gravity, planets nearer the Sun move faster, covering their orbit quicker.

4) Comets are also held in orbit by gravity, as are moons and satellites and space stations.

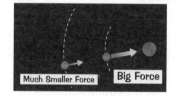

Much Smaller Force   Big Force

5) The size of the force of gravity decreases very quickly with increasing distance. E.g. if you double the distance of an object from a planet, the size of the force on it will be four times less.

In Practice That Means...

1) A long way out from the Sun, where Uranus orbits, the Sun's gravitational effect is weaker than here on Earth. So Uranus has a bigger orbit, travels slower and takes longer to complete its orbit than Earth.

2) Likewise, further in towards the Sun, its gravitational effect is stronger. Mercury is nearer the Sun than Earth, so it has a smaller orbit, travels faster and takes less time to complete its orbit than Earth.

Example: Look at the following table of data.
Is Planet X closer to or further away from the Sun than Earth?

planet	orbital period (earth days)	distance from Sun (km)
Mercury	88	57 910 000
Earth	365	149 600 000
Mars	687	227 940 000
Uranus	30685	2 870 990 000
Planet X	4333	not given

Planet X has a longer orbital period than Earth. A longer orbital period means a slower orbit speed and a bigger orbit, i.e. a bigger distance from the Sun.

(Even without knowing the theory, you could probably work that out from the table — so remember that if you're stuck in the exam.)

Imagine living on Mercury — Christmas every 88 days...

Everything on this page follows from the last page:
Once you learn that the closer to the Sun the stronger the gravity... and that the stronger the gravity the faster the circular motion... you know that the fast orbits mean near the Sun. Right? Right.

Gravity and Planetary Orbits

<u>Artificial satellites</u> were sent up by humans for <u>four</u> main purposes:

1) Monitoring of the Earth, e.g. <u>weather</u> and climate.
2) <u>Communications</u>, e.g. phone and **TV**.
3) <u>Space research</u> such as the Hubble Space Telescope.
4) <u>Spying</u> on baddies.

There are <u>two main kinds of orbits</u> useful for satellites:

1) Geostationary Satellites are Used for Communications

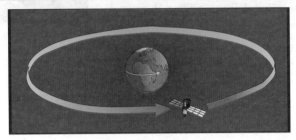

1) <u>Geostationary satellites</u> are in <u>high orbits</u> over the <u>equator</u> which take <u>exactly 24 hours</u> to complete.

2) This means that they <u>stay above the same point</u> on the Earth's surface because the Earth <u>rotates with them</u> — hence the name geo(Earth)-stationary.

3) This makes them <u>ideal</u> for <u>telephone</u> and <u>TV</u> because they're always in the <u>same place</u> and they can <u>transfer signals</u> from one side of the Earth to another in a <u>fraction of a second</u>.

2) Low Polar Orbit Satellites are for Weather and Spying

1) In a <u>low polar orbit</u>, the satellite sweeps over <u>both poles</u> whilst the Earth <u>rotates beneath it</u>.

2) The time taken for each full orbit is just <u>a few hours</u>.

3) Each time the satellite comes round it can <u>scan</u> the next bit of the globe.

4) This allows the <u>whole surface</u> of the planet to be <u>monitored</u> each day.

5) Geostationary satellites are <u>too high</u> to take good weather or spying photos, but the satellites in <u>polar orbits</u> are <u>nice and low</u>.

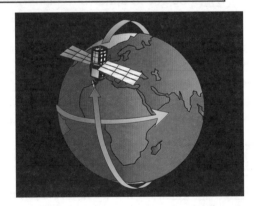

Example

The table gives data about two satellites.

Q1: Which satellite would be more useful for transmitting TV signals? Why?

Q2: Which satellite would be most useful for monitoring Earth's weather? Why?

	Orbital period (in Earth days)	Distance from Earth (km)	Position
Satellite A	0.07	800	Pole to pole
Satellite B	1	35 800	Around equator

<u>Satellite B</u> would be most useful for transmitting TV signals. This satellite is in a high orbit around the equator which takes exactly one day — so it's in a <u>geostationary</u> orbit.

<u>Satellite A</u> would be most useful for monitoring Earth's weather. This satellite is in a fast, low orbit. It sweeps over both poles (i.e. a polar orbit) as the Earth rotates, scanning the whole Earth.

Learn about satellites — and look down on your friends...

There are other kinds of satellites as well, e.g. GPS (Global Positioning System) satellites, which are in a different kind of orbit altogether. They work by transmitting their position and the time. These signals are received by GPS devices in cars or whatever, and once 4 signals have been received, the device can work out its exact location. It's all clever stuff. And you don't need to learn it, which is even better.

Images

You've already seen an application of total internal reflection in Physics 1b. This bit is all about how light behaves when it hits a lens or mirror. Be prepared for lots of diagrams on the next few pages.

A Real Image is Actually There — A Virtual Image Is Not

1) A real image is where the light from an object comes together to form an image on a 'screen' — like the image formed on an eye's retina (the 'screen' at the back of an eye).

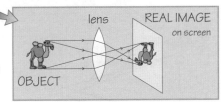

2) A virtual image is when the rays are diverging, so the light from the object appears to be coming from a completely different place.

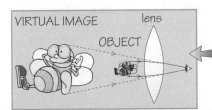

3) When you look in a mirror you see a virtual image of your face — because the object (your face) appears to be behind the mirror.

4) You can get a virtual image when looking at an object through a magnifying lens — the virtual image looks bigger and further away than the object actually is.

To describe an image properly, you need to say 3 things: 1) How big it is compared to the object; 2) Whether it's upright or inverted (upside down); 3) Whether it's real or virtual.

Reflection of Light Lets Us See Things

1) Reflection of light is what allows us to see objects. Light bounces off them into our eyes.

2) When light reflects from an uneven surface such as a piece of paper the light reflects off at all different angles and you get a diffuse reflection.

3) When light reflects from an even surface (smooth and shiny like a mirror) then it's all reflected at the same angle and you get a clear reflection.

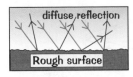

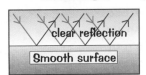

The normal is an imaginary line that's at right angles to the surface (at the point where the light hits the surface).

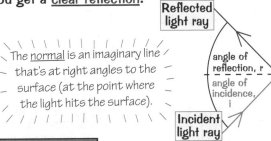

4) But don't forget, the LAW OF REFLECTION applies to every reflected ray:

Angle of INCIDENCE = Angle of REFLECTION

Note that these two angles are ALWAYS defined between the ray itself and the dotted NORMAL. Don't ever label them as the angle between the ray and the surface. Definitely uncool.

Refraction — Light Bends as it Changes Speed

1) Refraction of light is when the waves change direction as they enter a different medium.

2) This is caused entirely by the change in speed of the waves.

3) That's what makes ponds look shallower than they are — light reflects off the bottom and speeds up when it leaves the water, making the bottom look like it's nearer than it is:

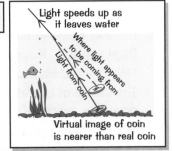

Light speeds up as it leaves water

Where light appears to be coming from

Light from coin

Virtual image of coin is nearer than real coin

Learn this now — and make light work of it in the exam...

Make sure you've learnt this little lot well enough to answer typical mean exam questions like these: "Explain why you can see a piece of paper" "What is diffuse reflection?" "Why is the image in a plane mirror virtual?" "Why do light rays bend as they leave a pond?"

Mirrors

The examiners do like to see a nice diagram, so get your rulers out.

Draw a Ray Diagram for an Image in a Plane Mirror

You need to be able to <u>reproduce</u> this entire diagram of <u>how an image is formed</u> in a <u>PLANE MIRROR</u>.

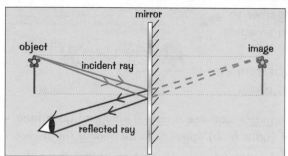

Learn these <u>three important points</u>:

1) The <u>image</u> is the <u>same size</u> as the <u>object</u>.
2) It is <u>AS FAR BEHIND</u> the mirror as the object is <u>in front</u>.
3) It's formed from <u>diverging rays</u>, which means it's a <u>virtual image</u>.

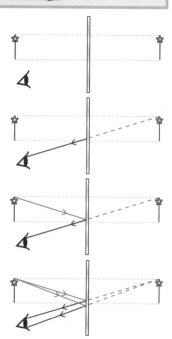

1) First off, draw the <u>virtual image</u>. <u>Don't</u> try to draw the rays first. Follow the rules in the above box — the image is the <u>same size</u>, and it's <u>as far behind</u> the mirror as the object is in <u>front</u>.

2) Next, draw a <u>reflected ray</u> going from the top of the virtual image to the top of the eye. Draw a <u>bold line</u> for the part of the ray between the mirror and eye, and a <u>dotted line</u> for the part of the ray between the mirror and virtual image.

3) Now draw the <u>incident ray</u> going from the top of the object to the mirror. The incident and reflected rays follow the <u>law of reflection</u> — but you <u>don't</u> actually have to measure any angles. Just draw the ray from the <u>object</u> to the <u>point</u> where the reflected ray <u>meets the mirror</u>.

4) Now you have an <u>incident ray</u> and <u>reflected ray</u> for the <u>top</u> of the image. Do <u>steps 2 and 3 again</u> for the <u>bottom</u> of the eye — reflected ray going from the image to the bottom of the eye, then an incident ray from the object to the mirror.

Curved Mirrors Are a Little More Complicated

<u>Concave</u> mirrors are shiny on the <u>inside</u> of the curve and <u>convex</u> mirrors are shiny on the <u>outside</u>. Light shining on a <u>concave</u> mirror <u>converges</u>, and light shining on a <u>convex</u> mirror <u>diverges</u>.

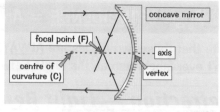

1) Uniformly curved mirrors are like a round portion of a <u>sphere</u>. The centre of the sphere is the <u>centre of curvature</u>, C.

2) The centre of the mirror's surface is called the <u>vertex</u>.

3) Halfway between the centre of curvature and the vertex is the <u>focal point</u>, F. Rays parallel to the axis of a concave mirror reflect and <u>meet at the focal point</u>.

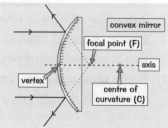

4) The centre of curvature, vertex and focal point all lie on a line down the <u>middle of the mirror</u> called the <u>axis</u>.

5) The centre of curvature and focal point are in <u>front</u> of a <u>concave</u> mirror, and <u>behind</u> a <u>convex</u> mirror.

Reflect on this for a while, pal...

Reflection in a plane (flat) mirror is not too horrendous. Learn the method <u>step by step</u> — doing it image first instead of rays first gives you a nice neat diagram, even if it seems weird to do it that way round. <u>Learn all the facts</u> about curved mirrors — it'll make the next page a load easier.

Physics 3(i) — Forces and Waves

Mirrors

You also could get asked to draw a ray diagram of reflection in a curved mirror. Pay attention, it's tricky.

Draw a Ray Diagram for an Image in a Concave Mirror

> 1) An incident ray parallel to the axis will pass through the focal point when it's reflected.
> 2) An incident ray passing through the focal point will be parallel to the axis when it's reflected.

1) Pick a point on the top of the object. Draw a ray going from the object to the mirror parallel to the axis of the mirror.

2) Draw another line going from the top of the object to the mirror, passing through the focal point on the way.

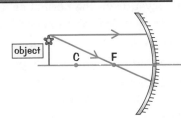

3) The incident ray that's parallel to the axis is reflected through the focal point. Draw a reflected ray passing through the focal point.

4) The incident ray that passes through the focal point is reflected parallel to the axis. Draw a reflected ray passing parallel to the axis.

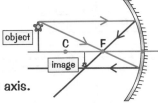

5) Mark where the two reflected rays meet. That's the top of the image.

6) Repeat the process for a point on the bottom of the object. When the bottom of the object is on the axis, the bottom of the image is also on the axis.

Distance from the Mirror Affects the Image

1) With an object at C (centre of curvature), you get a real, upside down image the same size as the object, in the same place.

2) Between C and F, you get a real, upside down image bigger than the object, and behind it.

3) An object in front of F makes a virtual image the right way up, bigger than F, behind the mirror. So hold it in front of F for doing your eyeliner.

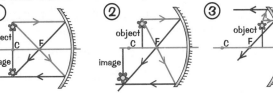

Draw a Ray Diagram for an Image in a Convex Mirror

> 1) An incident ray parallel to the axis will reflect so that the reflected ray seems to come from the focal point.
> 2) An incident ray that can be extended to pass through the focal point will be parallel to the axis when it's reflected.

Always extend the lines far enough behind the mirror to be sure they pass through the focal point if they need to.

1) Pick a point on the top of the object. Draw a ray going from the object to the mirror parallel to the axis of the mirror. Make it a bold line when it's in front of the mirror, and a dotted line when it's behind.

2) Draw another line going from the top of the object to the mirror, passing through the focal point on the other side. Make it dotted when it's behind the mirror.

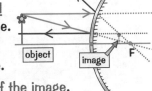

3) The incident ray that's parallel to the axis is reflected as if it starts at the focal point. Make sure the reflected ray meets the incident ray at the mirror surface.

4) The incident ray that passes through the focal point is reflected parallel to the axis. Make sure the reflected ray meets the incident ray at the mirror surface.

5) Mark where these two reflected rays meet behind the mirror. That's the top of the image.

6) Repeat the process for a point on the bottom of the object.

The Image is Always Smaller

1) The image in a convex mirror is always virtual, upright, smaller than the object and behind the mirror, closer than F. The further away the object is from the mirror, the smaller the image.

2) You can see a wide area in a convex mirror, which is why they put them on dodgy road corners.

Lenses

Lenses are usually made of glass or plastic. All lenses change the direction of light rays by refraction.

Light is Refracted When it Enters and Leaves Glass Prisms

You can't fail to remember the "ray of light through a rectangular glass block" trick:

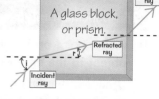

1) The ray bends towards the normal as it enters the denser medium, and away from the normal as it emerges into the less dense medium. Try to visualise the shape of the wiggle in the diagram — that can be easier than remembering the rule in words.

2) Note that different wavelengths of light refract by different amounts. So white light disperses into different colours as it enters a prism. A rectangular prism has parallel boundaries, so the rays bend one way as they enter, and then bend back again by the same amount as they leave — so white light emerges. But with a triangular prism, the boundaries aren't parallel, which means the different wavelengths don't recombine, and you get a nice rainbow effect.

Different Lenses Produce Different Kinds of Image

There are two main types of lens — converging and diverging. They have different shapes and have opposite effects on light rays.

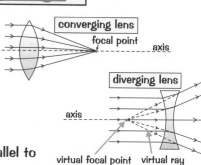

1) A converging lens is convex — it bulges outwards. It causes parallel rays of light to converge (move together) to a focus.

2) A diverging lens is concave — it caves inwards. It causes parallel rays of light to diverge (spread out).

3) The axis of a lens is a line passing through the middle of the lens.

4) The focal point of a converging lens is where rays hitting the lens parallel to the axis all meet.

5) The focal point of a diverging lens is the point where rays hitting the lens parallel to the axis appear to all come from — you can trace them back until they all appear to meet up at a point behind the lens.

6) Each lens has a focal point in front of the lens, and one behind.

There are Three Rules for Refraction in a Converging Lens...

1) An incident ray parallel to the axis refracts through the lens and passes through the focal point on the other side.

2) An incident ray passing through the focal point refracts through the lens and travels parallel to the axis.

3) An incident ray passing through the centre of the lens carries on in the same direction.

See next page for more on this.

... And Three Rules for Refraction in a Diverging Lens

1) An incident ray parallel to the axis refracts through the lens, and travels in line with the focal point (so it appears to have come from the focal point).

2) An incident ray passing towards the focal point refracts through the lens and travels parallel to the axis.

3) An incident ray passing through the centre of the lens carries on in the same direction.

See next page for more on this.

The neat thing about these rules is that they allow you to draw ray diagrams without bending the rays as they go into the lens and as they leave the lens. You can draw the diagrams as if each ray only changes direction once, in the middle of the lens.

Revise refraction — but don't let it slow you down...

Make sure that you can scribble a decent version of the glass block diagram — if you know it, it's easy marks. Then learn all the facts about converging and diverging lenses and the rules for refraction.

Lenses

You might have to draw a ray diagram of refraction through a lens. Follow the instructions very carefully...

Draw a Ray Diagram for an Image Through a Converging Lens

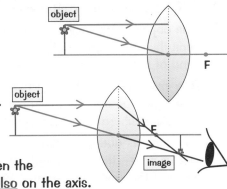

1) Pick a point on the <u>top</u> of the object. Draw a ray going from the object to the lens <u>parallel</u> to the axis of the lens.

2) Draw another ray from the top of the object going right through the middle of the lens.

3) The incident ray that's <u>parallel</u> to the axis is <u>refracted</u> through the <u>focal point</u>. Draw a <u>refracted ray</u> passing through the <u>focal point</u>.

4) The ray passing through the <u>middle</u> of the lens doesn't bend.

5) Mark where the rays <u>meet</u>. That's the <u>top of the image</u>.

6) Repeat the process for a point on the bottom of the object. When the bottom of the object is on the <u>axis</u>, the bottom of the image is <u>also</u> on the axis.

> If you <u>really</u> want to draw a <u>third incident ray</u> passing through the <u>focal point</u> on the way to the lens, you can (refract it so that it goes <u>parallel to the axis</u>). In the <u>exam</u>, you can get away with <u>two rays</u>, so no need to bother with three.

\\\ \ \ \ | | | / / / /
\ Watch out for tricky exam questions. /
~ This eye won't see all of the image — ~
– the ray from the bottom of the object –
/ doesn't quite meet the eye. \
/ / / / / | | | \ \ \ \ \

Distance from the Lens Affects the Image

1) An object <u>at 2F</u> will produce a <u>real</u>, <u>upside down</u> image the <u>same size</u> as the object, and <u>at 2F</u>.

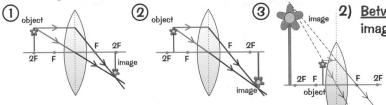

2) <u>Between F and 2F</u> it'll make a <u>real</u>, <u>upside down</u> image <u>bigger</u> than the object, and <u>beyond 2F</u>.

3) An object <u>nearer than F</u> will make a <u>virtual</u> image the <u>right way up</u>, <u>bigger</u> than the object, on the <u>same side</u> of the lens.

Draw a Ray Diagram for an Image Through a Diverging Lens

1) Pick a point on the <u>top</u> of the object. Draw a ray going from the object to the lens <u>parallel</u> to the axis of the lens.

2) Draw another ray from the top of the object going right through the middle of the lens.

3) The incident ray that's <u>parallel</u> to the axis is <u>refracted</u> so it appears to have come from the <u>focal point</u>. Draw a <u>ray</u> from the focal point. Make it <u>dotted</u> before it reaches the lens.

4) The ray passing through the <u>middle</u> of the lens doesn't bend.

5) Mark where the refracted rays <u>meet</u>. That's the top of the image.

6) Repeat the process for a point on the bottom of the object. When the bottom of the object is on the <u>axis</u>, the bottom of the image is <u>also</u> on the axis.

> Again, if you <u>really</u> want to draw a <u>third incident ray</u> in the direction of the <u>focal point</u> on the far side of the lens, you can. Remember to refract it so that it goes <u>parallel to the axis</u>. In the <u>exam</u>, you can get away with <u>two rays</u>. Choose whichever two are easiest to draw — don't try to draw a ray that won't actually pass through the lens.

The Image is Always Virtual

1) A diverging lens always produces a <u>virtual image</u>.

2) The image is <u>right way up</u>, <u>smaller</u> than the object and on the <u>same side of the lens as the object</u> — <u>no matter where the object is</u>.

Uses — Magnification and Cameras

Converging lenses are used in magnifying glasses and in cameras.

Magnifying Glasses Use Convex Lenses

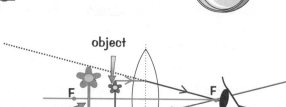

Magnifying glasses work by creating a magnified virtual image.

1) The object being magnified must be closer to the lens than the focal length (or you get a different kind of image — see diagrams on page 51).

2) The image produced is a virtual image. The light rays don't actually come from the place where the image appears to be.

3) Remember "you can't project a virtual image onto a screen" — that's a useful phrase to use in the exam if they ask you about virtual images.

Learn the Magnification Formula

You can use the magnification formula to work out the magnification produced by a lens or a mirror at a given distance:

$$\text{Magnification} = \frac{\text{image height}}{\text{object height}}$$

Example: A coin with diameter 14 mm is placed a certain distance behind a magnifying lens. The virtual image produced has a diameter of 35 mm. What is the magnification of the lens at this distance?

magnification = 35 ÷ 14
= 2.5

In the exam you might have to draw a ray diagram to show where an image would be, and then measure the image so that you can work out the magnification of the lens or mirror. Another reason to draw those ray diagrams carefully...

Taking a Photo Forms an Image on the Film

When you take a photograph of a flower, light from the object (flower) travels to the camera and is refracted by the lens, forming an image on the film.

1) The image on the film is a real image because light rays actually meet there.

2) The image is smaller than the object, because the object's a lot further away than the focal length of the lens.

3) The image is inverted — upside down.

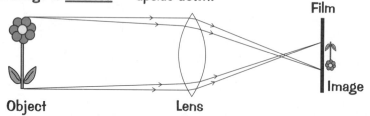

4) The same thing happens in our eye — a real, inverted image forms on the retina. Our very clever brains flip the image so that we see it right way up.

Picture this — you've revised it, and it turns up on the exam...

They're quite keen on making sure you know what all this Physics is actually used for. In this case, it's the joys of magnifying glasses and cameras. Scribble down a quick mini-essay on lenses in magnifying glasses, and one on lenses in cameras. And learn the formula.

Sound Waves

We hear sounds when vibrations reach our eardrums. You'll need to know how sound waves work.

Sound Travels as a Wave

1) <u>Sound waves</u> are caused by <u>vibrating objects</u>.
   These mechanical vibrations are passed through the
   surrounding medium as a series of compressions.
   They're known as <u>longitudinal waves</u>.

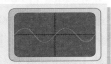

2) Sometimes the sound will eventually reach someone's <u>eardrum</u>,
   at which point the person might <u>hear it</u> (if it's loud enough and in the right frequency range — see below).

3) Because sound waves are caused by vibrating particles, the <u>denser</u> the medium, the <u>faster</u> sound
   travels through it, generally speaking anyway. Sound generally travels <u>faster in solids</u> than in liquids,
   and faster in liquids than in gases.

> Don't get confused by CRO displays (see next page), which show a transverse wave
> (like a water wave) when displaying sounds. The real sound wave is longitudinal —
> the display shows a transverse wave just so you can see what's going on.

Sound Waves Can Reflect and Refract

1) Sound waves will be <u>reflected</u> by <u>hard flat surfaces</u>. Things like <u>carpets</u> and <u>curtains</u> act as <u>absorbing surfaces</u> which will <u>absorb</u> sounds rather than reflect them.

2) This is very noticeable in an <u>empty room</u>. A big empty room sounds <u>completely different</u> once you've
   put carpet and curtains in, and a bit of furniture, because these things absorb the sound quickly and
   stop it <u>echoing</u> around the room.

3) <u>Sound waves</u> will also refract (change direction) as they enter <u>different media</u>.
   As they enter <u>denser</u> material, they <u>speed up</u>.
   (However, since sound waves are always <u>spreading out so much</u>,
   the change in direction is <u>hard to spot</u> under normal circumstances.)

We Hear Sounds in the Range 20 – 20 000 Hz

1) The <u>frequency</u> of a wave (in Hz) is the <u>number of waves</u> in 1 second.

2) The <u>human ear</u> is capable of hearing sounds with frequencies between <u>20 Hz</u> and <u>20 000 Hz</u>.
   (Although in practice some people can't hear some of the higher frequency sounds.)

Sound Does Not Travel in a Vacuum

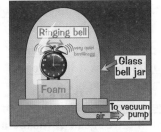

1) Sound waves are transmitted by vibrating particles — so they
   <u>can't travel</u> through a <u>vacuum</u>. (No particles, see.)

2) This is <u>nicely demonstrated</u> by the jolly old <u>bell jar experiment</u>.

3) As the <u>air is sucked out</u> by the <u>vacuum pump</u>, the sound gets
   <u>quieter and quieter</u>.

4) The bell has to be <u>mounted</u> on something like <u>foam</u> to stop the sound from it travelling through the
   solid surface and making the base vibrate, because you'd hear that instead.

So — does a falling tree make a sound if no one hears it?...

Eee by crumbs, we're off Light and onto Sound now. The thing to do here is learn the facts.
There's a simple equation that says <u>the more you learn now</u>, the <u>more marks you'll get</u> in the exam.
A lot of questions just test whether you've learned the facts. Easy marks, really.

Sound Waves

All sounds have <u>pitch</u> and <u>loudness</u>. Pitch and loudness can both be measured.

Loudness Increases with Amplitude

1) The <u>greater the amplitude</u> of a wave, the <u>more energy</u> it carries.
2) In <u>sound</u> this means it'll be <u>louder</u>.
3) <u>Bigger amplitude</u> means a <u>louder sound</u>.

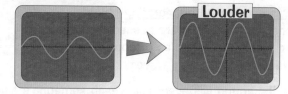

The Higher the Frequency, the Higher the Pitch

1) <u>High frequency</u> sound waves sound <u>high pitched</u> like a <u>squeaking mouse</u>.
2) <u>Low frequency</u> sound waves sound <u>low pitched</u> like a <u>mooing cow</u>.
3) <u>Frequency</u> is the number of <u>complete vibrations</u> each second.
4) Common <u>units</u> are <u>kHz</u> (1000 Hz) and <u>MHz</u> (1 000 000 Hz).
5) <u>High frequency</u> (or high pitch) also means <u>shorter wavelength</u>.
6) These <u>CRO traces</u> are <u>very important</u>, so make sure you know all about them:

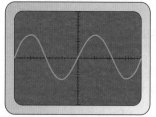
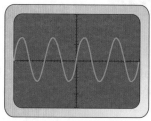
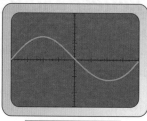
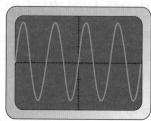

Original Sound | Higher pitched | Lower pitched | Higher pitched and louder

The Quality of a Note Depends on the Waveform

On a CRO trace, a clear, pure sound produces a smooth, rounded waveform called a <u>sine wave</u>.

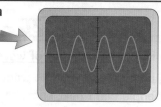

sine wave — clear, pure sound

Other kinds of sounds produce different CRO traces, e.g.:

1) Buzzy, brassy sounds have a <u>sawtooth waveform</u>, either with sloping "ups" and vertical "downs" or vertical "ups" and sloping "downs".

2) A waveform of <u>rectangular peaks and troughs</u> makes a thin, <u>reedy</u> sound, a bit like an oboe.

3) A <u>square wave</u> has peaks the same length as the troughs. It makes a <u>hollow</u> sound.

sawtooth wave — buzzy, brassy sound | pulse wave — thin, reedy sound | square wave — hollow sound | triangle wave — weak and mellow

4) Triangle waves are similar to sine waves, but they make a weaker, more mellow sound.

The quality of the note depends on how shaky your writing is...

The <u>important</u> things to remember here are what makes sounds <u>higher and lower pitched</u> and what makes sounds <u>louder and softer</u>. Once that's under your belt, have a think about the different shapes you get for different sounds. You don't need to learn all the shapes, just be aware there are differences.

Ultrasound

There's sound, and then there's ultrasound.

Ultrasound is Sound with a Higher Frequency than We Can Hear

Electrical devices can be made which produce <u>electrical oscillations</u> of <u>any frequency</u>. These can easily be converted into <u>mechanical vibrations</u> to produce <u>sound</u> waves <u>beyond the range of human hearing</u> (i.e. frequencies above 20 kHz). This is called <u>ultrasound</u> and it has loads of uses:

You Can Use CRO Traces to Compare Amplitudes and Frequencies

On the screen, CRO traces of ultrasound can look just like CRO traces for <u>normal pitched</u> sounds.

For showing high frequency ultrasound, the CRO is set so that <u>each square</u> on the screen corresponds to a <u>very short time</u>, e.g. <u>1 μs</u> (0.000 001 s). This lets you see each peak and trough:

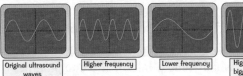

Original ultrasound waves | Higher frequency | Lower frequency | Higher frequency, bigger amplitude

Ultrasound Waves Get Partially Reflected at a Boundary Between Media

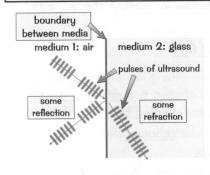

boundary between media
medium 1: air | medium 2: glass
pulses of ultrasound
some reflection | some refraction

1) When a wave passes from one medium into another, <u>some</u> of the wave is <u>reflected</u> off the boundary between the two media, and some is transmitted (and refracted). This is <u>partial reflection</u>.

2) What this means is that you can point a pulse of ultrasound at an object, and wherever there are <u>boundaries</u> between one substance and another, some of the ultrasound gets <u>reflected back</u>.

3) The time it takes for the reflections to reach a <u>detector</u> can be used to measure <u>how far away</u> the boundary is.

4) This is how <u>ultrasound imaging</u> works — see page 56.

You Can Use Oscilloscope Traces to Find Boundaries

1) The CRO trace on the right shows an ultrasound pulse reflecting off <u>two separate boundaries</u>.

2) Given the "seconds per division" setting of the CRO, you can work out the <u>time</u> between the pulses by measuring on the screen.

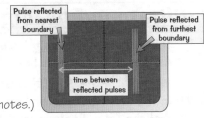

Pulse reflected from nearest boundary | Pulse reflected from furthest boundary
time between reflected pulses

3) Given the <u>speed of sound</u> in the medium, you can work out the <u>distance</u> between the boundaries, using $d = v \times t$.

4) They <u>might</u> give you the <u>frequency</u> and <u>wavelength</u> of the ultrasound and leave <u>you</u> to work out the speed using $v = f\lambda$. *(See your Physics 1b notes.)*

Example: A pulse of ultrasound is beamed into a person's abdomen. The first boundary it reflects off is between fat and muscle. The second boundary is between muscle and a body cavity. A CRO trace shows that the time between the reflected pulses is 10 μs. The frequency of ultrasound used is 30 kHz, and the wavelength is 5 cm. Calculate the distance between the fat/muscle boundary and the muscle/cavity boundary, to give you the thickness of the muscle layer.

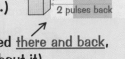

Pulse sent
2 pulses back

First work out the <u>speed</u> of the ultrasound using $v = f\lambda$. (Convert to Hz and m first.)
$v = 30\,000$ Hz $\times 0.05$ m. $v = 1500$ m/s.
Next you'll find the distance using $d = v \times t$. BUT, the reflected pulses have travelled <u>there and back</u>, so the distance you calculate will be <u>twice the distance between boundaries</u> (think about it).
So: $d = v \times t = 1500 \times (1 \times 10^{-5}) = 0.015$ m. So the distance between boundaries
(i.e. thickness of muscle layer) $= 0.015 \div 2 = 0.0075$ m $= \underline{7.5 \text{ mm}}$.

With reflections you always get a factor of 2... factor of 2...

Slightly trickier page here. Get the facts straight first — learn what ultrasound is, and what partial reflection is. Then make sure you can do the example question.

Ultrasound

Ultrasound has loads of exciting uses, including cleaning, quality control, pre-natal scans, and bats.

Ultrasound Vibrations are Used in Industrial Cleaning

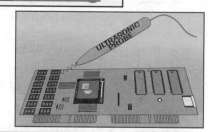

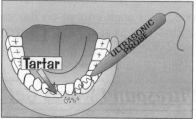

1) Ultrasound can be used to clean delicate mechanisms without them having to be dismantled.

2) Ultrasound waves can be directed onto very precise areas, and they're extremely effective at removing dirt and other deposits which form on delicate equipment.

3) The high frequency vibrations of ultrasound make the components of a piece of equipment vibrate at a high frequency. The dirt on the equipment vibrates too.

4) This vibration breaks up dirt and crud into very small particles, which simply fall off the equipment.

5) Alternatives to ultrasound would either damage the equipment (potentially), or require it to be dismantled before cleaning.

6) The same technique is sometimes used by dentists to clean teeth.

Ultrasound is Used in Industrial Quality Control

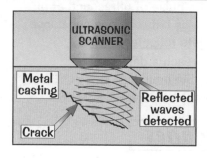

1) Ultrasound waves can pass through something like a metal casting and whenever they reach a boundary between two different media (like metal and air) some of the wave is reflected back and detected.

2) The exact timing and distribution of these echoes gives detailed information about the internal structure.

3) The echoes are usually processed by computer to produce a visual display of what the object must be like inside. If there are cracks where there shouldn't be, they'll show up.

Ultrasound Imaging is Used for Pre-Natal Scanning of a Fetus

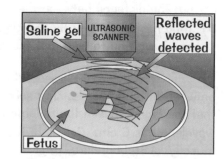

1) This follows the same principle as the industrial quality control. As the ultrasound hits boundaries between different media some of the wave is reflected back.

2) In the uterus, there are boundaries between the amniotic fluid that the fetus floats in, and the body tissues of the fetus itself.

3) The reflected waves are processed by computer to produce a video image of the fetus.

4) The video image can be used to see if the fetus is developing correctly — and sometimes what sex the fetus is.

5) No one knows for sure whether ultrasound is safe in all cases, but X-rays would definitely be dangerous to the fetus.

 Bats use a similar technique. They send out ultrasound squeaks, and pick up the reflections with their enormous ears. Their brains process the reflected signals, and turn them into a picture of what's around. So basically, bats 'see' with sound waves.

Could do with an ultrasound cleaning ray in my house...

Bats are amazing, really. They can 'see' with ultrasound well enough to catch a moth in mid-flight in complete darkness. It's a nice trick if you can do it. Another nice trick, and a much easier one, is to learn everything on this page. Cover up the page and scribble some mini-essays, and see how you do.

Revision Summary for Physics 3(i)

Phew, hurrah, yay — made it to the end of this section. A lot of tricky ideas to remember — especially all that stuff on drawing ray diagrams for different mirrors and lenses. So, get yourself stuck into these revision questions to find out how much you've learnt...

1) Sarah is levering the lid off a can of paint using a screwdriver. She places the tip of the 20 cm long screwdriver under the can's lid and applies a force of 10 N on the end of the screwdriver's handle as shown. Suggest two ways that Sarah could increase the moment about the pivot point (the side of the can).

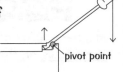
pivot point

2) Describe two different ways of finding the centre of mass of a rectangular playing card.

3)* Arthur weighs 600 N and is sitting on a seesaw 1.5 m from the pivot point. His friend Caroline weighs 450 N and sits on the seesaw so that it balances. How far from the pivot point is Caroline sitting?

4) A cyclist is moving at a constant speed of 5 m/s around a circular track.

   a) Is the cyclist accelerating? Explain your answer.

   b) What force keeps the cyclist travelling in a circle? Where does this force come from?

   c) What will happen to the size of this force if the same cyclist travels at a constant speed of 5 m/s around a different circular track that has a larger radius?

5) Gravity is the force of attraction between two masses. What happens to the size of this force if the distance between the masses decreases?

6) Two identical satellites orbit at different distances from the Earth. Satellite A orbits the Earth at a distance of 10 000 km and satellite B orbits at 20 000 km. Which satellite has the smaller orbital period? Explain your answer.

7) Name four uses for artificial satellites.

8) State three differences between a low polar orbit and a geostationary orbit.

9) What is a real image? How is it different from a virtual image?

10) A ray of light hits the surface of a mirror at an incident angle of 10° to the normal. What is the angle of reflection for the ray of light?

11) Describe the steps you would take to draw a ray diagram for an image in a plane mirror. Draw diagrams to illustrate your method.

12) Explain how the following rays of light are reflected:

   a) an incident ray parallel to the axis of a convex mirror.

   b) an incident ray passing through the focal point of a concave mirror.

13) Draw a diagram to show the path of a ray of light as it passes from air → block of glass → air, meeting the block of glass at an angle.

14)* Peter measures the length of a seed to be 1.5 cm. When he looks at the seed through a converging lens at a certain distance, the seed appears to have a length of 4.5 cm. What is the magnification of this lens at this distance?

15) Describe how a sound wave travels through a medium. What is this type of wave called?

16) Explain why sound travels faster through an iron bar than through the air.

17) This is a diagram of a sound wave displayed on an oscilloscope.

   a) What is happening to the loudness of this sound wave?

   b) What is happening to the pitch of this sound wave?

18)* An ultrasonic scanner above the ground is used to detect the depth of an underground water pipe at two different locations (A and B). For each location, the times between pulses reflected off the ground's surface and the top of the pipe are shown in the data table. The speed of the ultrasound is 2800 m/s. What is the depth of the pipe at its deepest point?

	Time between reflected pulses
Location A	0.002 seconds
Location B	0.003 seconds

* Answers on page 76.

Magnetic Fields

There's a proper definition of a <u>magnetic field</u> which you really ought to learn:

> A <u>MAGNETIC FIELD</u> is a region where <u>MAGNETIC MATERIALS</u> (like iron and steel)
> and also <u>WIRES CARRYING CURRENTS</u> experience <u>A FORCE</u> acting on them.

Magnetic fields can be represented by <u>field diagrams</u>.
<u>The arrows on the field lines always point FROM THE NORTH POLE of the magnet TO THE SOUTH POLE!</u>

The Magnetic Field Round a Current-Carrying Wire

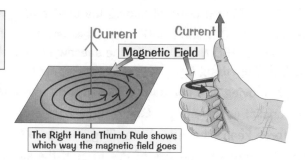

1) There is a magnetic field around a <u>straight</u>, <u>current-carrying wire</u>.

2) The field is made up of <u>concentric circles</u> with the wire in the centre.

The Right Hand Thumb Rule shows which way the magnetic field goes

The Magnetic Field Round a Solenoid

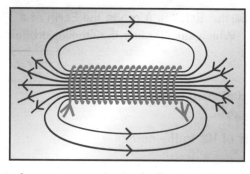

1) The magnetic field <u>inside</u> a <u>solenoid</u> (a coil of wire) is <u>strong</u> and <u>uniform</u>.

2) <u>Outside</u> the coil, the magnetic field is just like the one round a <u>bar magnet</u>.

3) This means that the <u>ends</u> of a solenoid act like the <u>north pole</u> and <u>south pole</u> of a bar magnet.

4) Pretty obviously, if the <u>direction</u> of the <u>current</u> is <u>reversed</u>, the N and S poles will <u>swap ends</u>.

5) If you imagine looking directly into one end of a solenoid, the <u>direction of current flow</u> tells you whether it's the <u>N or S pole</u> you're looking at, as shown by the <u>two diagrams</u> opposite.

6) You can increase the <u>strength</u> of the magnetic field around a solenoid by adding a magnetically <u>"soft"</u> iron core through the middle of the coil. It's then called an <u>ELECTROMAGNET</u>.

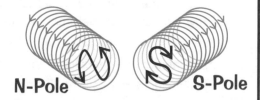

N-Pole   S-Pole

> A <u>magnetically soft</u> material <u>magnetises</u> and <u>demagnetises</u> very easily.
> So, as soon as you <u>turn off</u> the current through the solenoid, the
> magnetic field <u>disappears</u> — the iron doesn't stay magnetised.

Iron, Steel and Nickel are Magnetic

Don't forget that <u>all</u> other <u>common metals</u> are <u>not magnetic at all</u>. So a magnet <u>won't stick</u> to <u>aluminium ladders</u> or <u>copper kettles</u> or <u>brass trumpets</u> or <u>gold rings</u> or <u>silver spoons</u>.

Discovering electromagnetism — a compass pointed the way...

The <u>ancient Greeks</u> and <u>ancient Chinese</u> knew that lumps of magnetic rock would attract iron objects, and always point north-south — they could be used like a basic <u>compass</u>. It took until the early 1800s before the links between electricity and magnetism were discovered. Amazing.

The Motor Effect

Passing an electric current through a wire produces a magnetic field around the wire. If you put that wire into a magnetic field, you have <u>two magnetic fields combining</u>, which puts a force on the wire (generally).

A Current *in a* Magnetic Field Experiences a Force

The two tests below demonstrate the <u>force</u> on a <u>current-carrying wire</u> placed in a <u>magnetic field</u>. The <u>force</u> gets <u>bigger</u> if either the <u>current</u> or the <u>magnetic field</u> is made bigger.

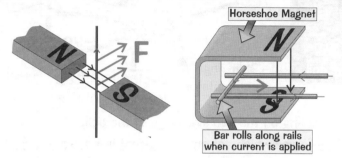

Horseshoe Magnet

Bar rolls along rails when current is applied

1) Note that in <u>both cases</u> the <u>force</u> on the wire is at <u>90°</u> to both the <u>wire</u> and to the <u>magnetic field</u>.
2) You can always <u>predict</u> which way the <u>force</u> will act using <u>Fleming's left hand rule</u> as shown below.
3) To experience the <u>full force</u>, the <u>wire</u> has to be at <u>90°</u> to the <u>magnetic field</u>.
4) If the wire runs <u>along</u> the <u>magnetic field</u> it won't experience <u>any force at all</u>.
5) At angles in between it'll feel <u>some</u> force.

Fleming's Left Hand Rule *Tells You* Which Way *the Force Acts*

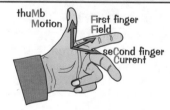

thuMb Motion
First finger Field
seCond finger Current

1) They could test if you can do this, so <u>practise it</u>.
2) Using your <u>left hand</u>, point your <u>First finger</u> in the direction of the <u>Field</u> and your <u>seCond finger</u> in the direction of the <u>Current</u>.
3) Your <u>thuMb</u> will then point in the direction of the <u>force</u> (<u>M</u>otion).

<u>EXAMPLE:</u> Which direction is the force on the wire?

<u>ANSWER:</u>

1) Draw in current arrows (+ve to –ve).

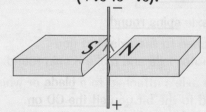

2) Fleming's LHR.

seCond finger Current
First finger Field
thuMb Motion

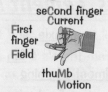

3) Draw in direction of force (motion).

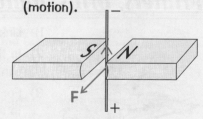

Remember the Left Hand Rule for Motors — drive on the left...

Always remember that it's the <u>LEFT</u> hand rule. If you whip your <u>right</u> hand out in the exam and start looking at the fingers, you'll get it <u>WRONG</u>. Remember that magnetic fields go from <u>north to south</u>, not south to north. And yes, it <u>seems weird</u> that magnets move wires, but that's Physics for you.

The Simple Electric Motor

Aha — one of the favourite exam topics of all time. Read it. Understand it. Learn it.

The Simple Electric Motor

4 Factors which Speed it up
1) More **CURRENT**
2) More **TURNS** on the coil
3) **STRONGER MAGNETIC FIELD**
4) A **SOFT IRON CORE** in the coil

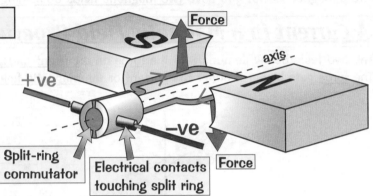

Force · axis · +ve · −ve · Force · Split-ring commutator · Electrical contacts touching split ring

1) The diagram shows the <u>forces</u> acting on the two <u>side arms</u> of the <u>coil</u>.

2) These forces are just the <u>usual forces</u> which act on <u>any current</u> in a <u>magnetic field</u>.

3) Because the coil is on a <u>spindle</u> and the forces act <u>one up</u> and <u>one down</u>, it <u>rotates</u>.

4) The <u>split-ring commutator</u> is a clever way of "<u>swapping</u> the contacts <u>every half turn</u> to keep the motor rotating in the <u>same direction</u>". (Learn that statement because they might ask you.)

5) The direction of the motor can be <u>reversed</u> either by swapping the <u>polarity</u> of the <u>DC supply</u> or swapping the <u>magnetic poles</u> over.

EXAMPLE: Is the coil turning clockwise or anticlockwise?

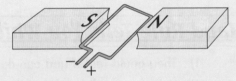

ANSWER:

| 1) Draw in current arrows (+ve to −ve). | 2) Fleming's LHR on one arm (I've used the right hand arm). | 3) Draw in direction of force (motion). |

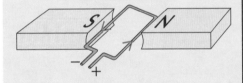

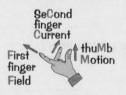
SeCond finger Current · First finger Field · thuMb Motion

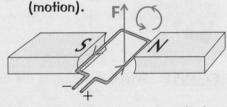
F↑
So — the coil is turning <u>anticlockwise</u>.

Electric Motors are used in:
CD Players, Food Mixers, Fan Heaters, Fans, Printers, Drills, Hairdriers, Cement Mixers...

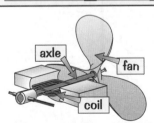
axle · fan · coil

1) Link the coil to an <u>axle</u>, and the axle <u>spins round</u>.

2) In the diagram there's a <u>fan</u> attached to the axle, but you can stick <u>almost anything</u> on a motor axle and make it spin round.

3) For example, in a <u>food mixer</u>, the axle's attached to a <u>blade</u> or whisks. In a <u>CD player</u> the axle's attached to the bit you <u>sit the CD on</u>. <u>Fan heaters</u> and <u>hairdriers</u> have an <u>electric heater</u> as well as a fan.

Hello Motor...

Loudspeakers also demonstrate the <u>motor effect</u>. <u>AC electrical signals</u> from the <u>amplifier</u> are fed to the <u>speaker coil</u> (shown red). These make the coil move <u>back and forth</u> over the poles of the <u>magnet</u>. These movements make the <u>cardboard cone vibrate</u> and this creates <u>sounds</u>.

Electromagnetic Induction

Sounds terrifying. Well, sure it's quite mysterious, but it isn't that complicated:

ELECTROMAGNETIC INDUCTION:
The creation of a **VOLTAGE** (and maybe current) in a wire which is experiencing a **CHANGE IN MAGNETIC FIELD**.

For some reason they use the word "induction" rather than "creation", but it amounts to the same thing.

Moving a Magnet in a Coil of Wire Induces a Voltage

1) Electromagnetic induction means creating a voltage (and maybe a current) in a conductor. You can do this by moving a magnet in a coil of wire or moving a conductor in a magnetic field ("cutting" magnetic field lines). Shifting the magnet from side to side creates a little "blip" of current.

A few examples of electromagnetic induction:

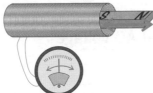
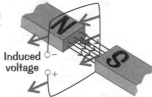
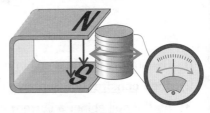

Induced voltage

2) If you move the magnet in the opposite direction, then the voltage/current will be reversed too. Likewise if the polarity of the magnet is reversed, then the voltage/current will be reversed too.

3) If you keep the magnet (or the coil) moving backwards and forwards, you produce a voltage that keeps swapping direction — and this is how you produce AC current.

You can create the same effect by turning a magnet end to end in a coil, to create a current that lasts as long as you spin the magnet. This is how generators work (see next page).

1) As you turn the magnet, the magnetic field through the coil changes — this change in the magnetic field induces a voltage, which can make a current flow in the wire.

2) When you've turned the magnet through half a turn, the direction of the magnetic field through the coil reverses. When this happens, the voltage reverses, so the current flows in the opposite direction around the coil of wire.

3) If you keep turning the magnet in the same direction — always clockwise, say — then the voltage will keep on reversing every half turn and you'll get an AC current.

Four Factors Affect the Size of the Induced Voltage

1) If you want a bigger peak voltage (and current) you have to increase at least one of these four things:

1) The **STRENGTH** of the **MAGNET**　　2) The **AREA** of the **COIL**
3) The **number of TURNS** on the **COIL**　　4) The **SPEED** of movement

2) To reduce the voltage, you would reduce one of those factors, obviously.

3) If you move the magnet faster, you'll get a higher peak voltage, but also get a higher frequency — because the magnetic field is reversing more frequently.

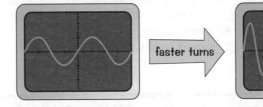

faster turns

EM Induction — works whether the coil or the field is moving...
"Electromagnetic Induction" gets my vote for "Definitely Most Tricky Topic". If it wasn't so important maybe you wouldn't have to bother learning it. The trouble is, this is how all our electricity is generated.

Generators

Generators do exactly what you'd expect them to do — they generate electricity. And it's all down to electromagnetic induction. You'll love it — it's electrifying stuff. Ho ho.

AC Generators — Just Turn the Coil and There's a Current

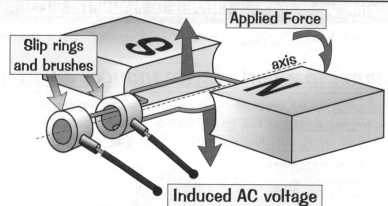

1) Generators rotate a coil in a magnetic field.

2) Their construction is pretty much like a motor.

3) As the coil spins, a current is induced in the coil. This current changes direction every half turn.

4) Instead of a split-ring commutator, generators have slip rings and brushes so the contacts don't swap every half turn.

5) This means they produce AC voltage, as shown by these CRO displays. Note that faster revs produce not only more peaks but higher overall voltage too.

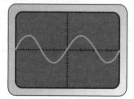

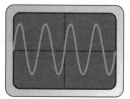

original   faster revs

Dynamos — You Turn the Magnet Instead of the Coil

1) Dynamos are a slightly different type of generator. They rotate the magnet instead of the coil.

2) This still causes the field through the coil to swap every half turn, so the output is just the same as for a generator.

3) This means you get the same CRO traces of course.

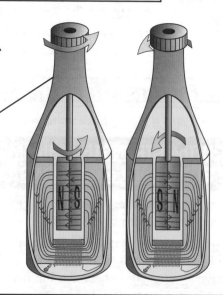

Dynamos are often used on bikes to power the lights. The cog wheel at the top is positioned so that it touches one of the wheels. As the wheel moves round, it turns the cog which is attached to the magnet. This creates an AC current to power the lights.

Dynamo Kiev — they like a bit of squad rotation...

The National Grid is fed by hundreds of generators. These are usually driven by steam turbines (and the steam usually comes from burning things). You can get small portable petrol generators too, to use where there's no mains electricity — on building sites, say.

Physics 3(ii) — Magnetism and Stars

Transformers

Transformers use electromagnetic induction. So they will only work on AC.

Transformers Change the Voltage — but Only AC Voltages

There are a few different types of transformer. The two you need to know about are step-up transformers and step-down transformers. They both have two coils, the primary and the secondary, joined with an iron core.

STEP-UP TRANSFORMERS step the voltage up. They have more turns on the secondary coil than the primary coil.

STEP-DOWN TRANSFORMERS step the voltage down. They have more turns on the primary coil than the secondary.

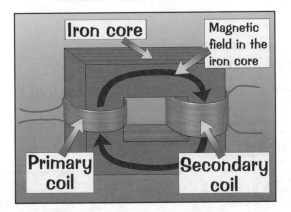

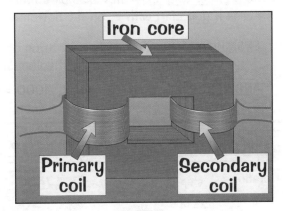

Transformers Work by Electromagnetic Induction

1) The primary coil produces a magnetic field which stays within the iron core. This means nearly all of it passes through the secondary coil and hardly any is lost.

2) Because there is alternating current (AC) in the primary coil, the field in the iron core is constantly changing direction (100 times a second if it's at 50 Hz) — i.e. it is a changing magnetic field.

3) This rapidly changing magnetic field is then felt by the secondary coil.

4) The changing field induces an alternating voltage in the secondary coil (with the same frequency as the alternating current in the primary) — electromagnetic induction of a voltage in fact.

5) The relative number of turns on the two coils determines whether the voltage induced in the secondary coil is greater or less than the voltage in the primary.

6) If you supplied DC to the primary, you'd get nothing out of the secondary at all. Sure, there'd still be a magnetic field in the iron core, but it wouldn't be constantly changing, so there'd be no induction in the secondary because you need a changing field to induce a voltage. Don't you! So don't forget it — transformers only work with AC. They won't work with DC at all.

The Iron Core Carries Magnetic Field, Not Current

1) The iron core is purely for transferring the changing magnetic field from the primary coil to the secondary.

2) No electricity flows round the iron core.

The ubiquitous Iron Core — where would we be without it...

Transformers only work with AC. I'll say that again. Transformers only work with AC. Prevent disaster in the exam by remembering the fact that transformers only work with AC. Now that's out of the way, I recommend you learn the details and the diagrams, then cover the page and scribble them down.

Transformers

The Transformer Equation — use it Either Way Up

You can calculate the output voltage from a transformer if you
know the input voltage and the number of turns on each coil.

| $\dfrac{\text{Primary Voltage}}{\text{Secondary Voltage}}$ | $=$ | $\dfrac{\text{Number of turns on Primary}}{\text{Number of turns on Secondary}}$ |

$$\frac{V_P}{V_S} = \frac{N_P}{N_S}$$

or

$$\frac{V_S}{V_P} = \frac{N_S}{N_P}$$

Well, it's just another formula. You stick in the numbers you've got
and work out the one that's left. It's really useful to remember you
can write it either way up — this example's much trickier
algebra-wise if you start with V_S on the bottom...

> **EXAMPLE:** A transformer has 40 turns on the primary and 800 on the
> secondary. If the input voltage is 1000 V, find the output voltage.
>
> **ANSWER:** $V_S/V_P = N_S/N_P$ so $V_S/1000 = 800/40$ $V_S = 1000 \times (800/40) = \underline{20\,000\text{ V}}$

Transformers are used on the National Grid

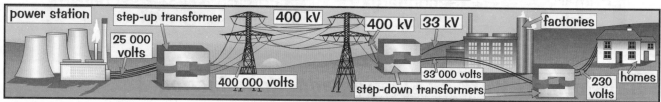

You get both step-up and step-down transformers on the National Grid:

1) To transmit a lot of power, you either need high voltage or high current ($P = VI$).

2) The problem with high current is the loss of power (as heat) due to the resistance of the cables.

3) The formula for power loss due to resistance in the cables is: $P = I^2R$ (from $P = VI$ and $V = IR$)

4) Because of the I^2 bit, if the current is 10 times bigger, the losses will be 100 times bigger.

5) It's much cheaper to boost the voltage up to 400 000 V and keep the current very low.

6) This requires transformers as well as big pylons with huge insulators, but it's still cheaper.

7) The transformers have to step the voltage up at one end, for efficient transmission, and then bring
it back down to safe, useable levels at the other end.

Choose the Right Transformer — is it Up or Down?

Remember, it's step-up when you need to increase the voltage, and step-down to decrease the voltage.

> **EXAMPLE:** A German tourist is visiting the United States. Domestic electricity supply in Germany
> is 230 V AC, and domestic electricity supply in the United States is 110 V AC.
> The tourist is bringing a laptop which needs 230 V AC when it's plugged in.
>
> State what kind of transformer the German tourist needs, and explain your answer.
>
> **ANSWER:** The tourist needs a step-up transformer.
> The 110 V supply needs to be stepped up to 230 V.

Which transformer do you need to enslave the Universe — Megatron...

You'll need to practise with those tricky equations. They're unusual because they can't be put into
formula triangles, but other than that the method is the same — stick in the numbers. Just practise.

Stars and Galaxies

Oooh... space. I reckon this is much more fun than electricity, so I've saved it for last. ☺

Stars and Solar Systems Form from Clouds of Gas and Dust

1) Stars form from clouds of gas and dust which spiral in together due to gravitational attraction.

2) Gravity compresses the matter so much that intense heat develops and sets off nuclear fusion reactions.
    The star then begins emitting light and other radiation.

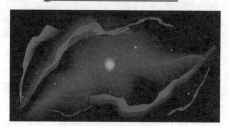

3) At the same time that the star is forming, other lumps may develop from the same spiralling cloud. These eventually gather together and form planets which orbit around the star.

Our Sun is in the Milky Way Galaxy

1) The Sun is one of many billions of stars which form the Milky Way galaxy.

2) The distance between neighbouring stars is usually hundreds of thousands of times greater than the distance between planets in our Solar System.

3) Gravity is of course the force which keeps the stars together in a galaxy and, like most things in the Universe, the galaxies all rotate, kinda like a catherine wheel only much slower.

4) Our Sun is about two thirds of the way out towards the end of one of the spiral arms of the Milky Way galaxy.

The Whole Universe has Billions of Galaxies

1) Galaxies themselves are often millions of times further apart than the stars are within a galaxy.

2) So all of you will soon begin to realise that the Universe is mostly empty space and is really really big. Have you ever been to the NEC? Yeah? Well, it's even bigger than that.

The Early Universe Contained Only Hydrogen

1) At the very beginning, just seconds after the Big Bang, there was only hydrogen (with some helium forming very soon after). As the Universe expanded, these atoms clumped together to form stars.

2) In the cores of stars, hydrogen nuclei smash together to form helium nuclei. This is nuclear fusion. As a star grows older, all the hydrogen in the core turns into helium.

3) Once the hydrogen has run out, helium nuclei fuse to form other, heavier elements. Three helium nuclei can combine to form one carbon nucleus. More helium nuclei combine with carbon nuclei to make oxygen and neon. This all happens in red giant stars (see page 66).

4) Eventually the helium in the core runs out, and some of the carbon, oxygen and neon combine to make silicon. In the very biggest stars, nuclei keep on combining by fusion until they've formed iron.

5) At the end of their lives, massive stars explode, flinging gas out into space. In these explosions, heavy nuclei combine with each other and with neutrons to make pretty much all the elements in the Universe.

6) The dust and gas from these supernova explosions can form new stars and planets (like ours). These second (or third, or fourth...) generation star systems contain heavier elements as well as hydrogen.

Just don't forget your towel...

More gripping facts about the Universe. Just look at those numbers: there's billions of stars in the Milky Way, the Universe contains billions of galaxies... All of the elements in the Universe were made in stars from hydrogen and helium... Doesn't it just blow your socks off...

66

The Life Cycle of Stars

Stars go through many traumatic stages in their lives — just like teenagers.

Clouds of Dust and Gas

1) Stars initially form from clouds of DUST and GAS.

Protostar

2) The force of gravity makes the gas clouds come spiralling in. As they do, gravitational energy is converted into heat energy and the temperature rises.

3) When the temperature gets high enough, hydrogen nuclei undergo nuclear fusion to form helium nuclei and give out massive amounts of heat and light. A star is born. It immediately enters a long stable period where the heat created by the nuclear fusion provides an outward pressure to balance the force of gravity pulling everything inwards. In this stable period it's called a MAIN SEQUENCE STAR. Because the balanced forces stop everything exploding outwards or collapsing inwards, and because of the huge amount of hydrogen stars contain, this stable period can last millions of years. (The Sun is in the middle of its stable period... or to put it another way, the Earth has already had half its innings before the Sun engulfs it!)

Main Sequence Star

4) Eventually the hydrogen begins to run out and the star then swells into a RED GIANT. It becomes red because the surface cools.

5) A small star like our Sun will then begin to cool and contract into a WHITE DWARF and then finally, as the light fades completely, it becomes a BLACK DWARF. (That's going to be really sad.)

Red Giant

Small stars → **White Dwarf** → **Black Dwarf**

Big stars

6) Big stars, however, start to glow brightly again as they undergo more fusion and expand and contract several times, forming heavier elements in various nuclear reactions. Eventually they'll explode in a SUPERNOVA.

new planetary nebula... ...and a new solar system

Supernova

Neutron Star...

7) The exploding supernova throws the outer layers of dust and gas into space, leaving a very dense core called a NEUTRON STAR. Or if the star is big enough, a BLACK HOLE.

...or Black Hole

8) The dust and gas thrown off by the supernova will form into SECOND GENERATION STARS like our Sun. The heavier elements are only made in the final stages of a big star, many in the supernova itself, so the presence of heavier elements in the Sun and the inner planets is clear evidence that our beautiful and wonderful world, with its warm sunsets and fresh morning dews, has all formed out of the snotty remains of a grisly old star's last dying sneeze.

9) The matter from which neutron stars and white dwarfs and black dwarfs are made is MILLIONS OF TIMES DENSER than any matter on Earth because the gravity is so strong it even crushes the atoms.

Revision Summary for Physics 3(ii)

Well, that's a section of two halves if I ever saw one. All that stuff about magnets and electricity is pretty tricky but really really important — so I reckon it's a good idea to make sure you know it back to front and inside out. And there's only one way to check you know it all. Sorry.

1) In which direction is the magnetic field around this wire — clockwise or anticlockwise?

2) Sketch a diagram showing the magnetic field around a solenoid.

3) Name the three common magnetic metals.

4) Describe the three details of Fleming's left hand rule. What is it used for?

5) Sketch a diagram of a simple motor. Indicate the direction in which the motor spins.

6) The diagrams show a simple electric motor. The coil is turning clockwise. Which diagram, A or B, shows the correct polarity of the magnets?

7) What are the four factors that affect the speed of a motor?

8) Name five devices that use an electric motor.

9) Give the definition of electromagnetic induction.

10) What are the four factors that affect the size of the induced voltage?

11) Sketch a generator with all the details. Explain how it works.

12) a) Describe how a dynamo works.
b)* Give a disadvantage of having bicycle lights powered by a dynamo.

13) Sketch the two types of transformer and explain the differences between them.

14) An engineering executive is travelling from the USA to Italy and taking a computer monitor with him. In the USA, domestic electricity is 110 V AC, and in Italy it's 230 V AC. What kind of transformer would the engineering executive need to plug his monitor into?

15) Explain how a transformer works and why transformers only work on AC voltage.

16) Write down the transformer equation.

17)* A transformer has 20 turns on the primary coil and 600 on the secondary coil. If the input voltage is 9 V, find the output voltage.

18) Explain why transformers are used on the National Grid.

19) Describe the first stages of a star's formation. Where does the initial energy come from?

20) What process starts inside a star to make it produce so much light and heat?

21) Sketch the Milky Way and show the Sun in relation to it.

22) How far away are stars from each other, compared to the distances between planets in our Solar System?

23) How far away are galaxies from each other, compared to the distances between stars in a galaxy?

24) Shortly after the Universe began, what was the most common element?

25) Briefly describe how elements like carbon, silicon and iron were formed.

26) What is the name given to a star during its long stable period?

27) Briefly explain how a star can keep producing light and heat for millions of years.

28) What is the final stage of a small star's life?

29) What is the final stage of a big star's life?

30) What is meant by a "second generation star"? How do we know that the Sun is one?

* Answers on page 76.

Exam Skills

Thinking in Exams

In the old days, it was enough to learn a whole bunch of <u>facts</u> while you were revising and just spew them onto the paper come exam day. If you knew the facts, you had a good chance of doing well, even if you didn't really <u>understand</u> what any of those facts actually meant. But those days are over. Rats.

Remember — You Might Have to Think During the Exam

1) Nowadays, the examiners want you to be able to <u>apply</u> your scientific knowledge and <u>understand articles</u> written about science. Eeek.

2) The trick is <u>not</u> to <u>panic</u>. They're <u>not</u> expecting you to show Einstein-like levels of scientific insight (not usually, anyway).

3) They're just expecting you to use the science you <u>know</u> in both <u>familiar</u> and <u>unfamiliar settings</u>. And sometimes they'll give you some <u>extra info</u> too that you should use in your answer.

So to give you an idea of what to expect come exam-time, use the new <u>CGP Exam Simulator</u> (below). Read the article, and have a go at the questions. It's <u>guaranteed</u> to be just as much fun as the real thing.

Underlining or making notes of the main bits as you read is a good idea.

1. Stopping distance divided into distance for thinking and braking

2. Distance varies
→ speed, driver, car

3. Car needs to have good grip on road... to improve stopping distances...

4. Grip on road
→ tyres
→ weather conditions
→ road surface

The distance it takes for a car to stop once the driver has seen a hazard is divided between the <u>thinking distance</u> and the <u>braking distance</u>. These two distances are affected by many factors, such as <u>how fast the car is going</u> and the <u>condition of the driver and the car</u>.

It's important for the car to have a <u>good grip</u> on the road. The better the grip the sooner the car will be able to stop. Tyres should have a <u>minimum tread depth</u> of 1.6 mm to have enough grip in wet conditions. Without any tread the tyre will just ride on the layer of water and skid really easily. Drivers should take extra care when it's <u>wet or icy</u> as the road's slippier than when it's dry. Even the <u>road surface</u> can make a difference — gravel, leaves and muck can all cause the car to slip.

Mark Smith, a director of GoodTyres plc, said: "We recommend regularly replacing your tyres for the best control of your car and better road safety."

<u>Questions:</u>

1. Why should a car owner check the tread depth of their car's tyres?

2. In rainy conditions, why should people leave a greater distance between their car and the car in front?

3. Why might some people suspect Mark Smith of being biased?

Clues — don't read unless you need a bit of a hand...
1. Think about what would happen if the tyres didn't have any tread.
2. What happens to the road surface in wet conditions? What effect will this have on the stopping distance?
3. What's his job?

Answers 3) He's a director of a firm that probably makes tyres — so he'll want to make them sound as important as possible.
2) In wet conditions there is more water on the road, which means the car has less grip. This increases the braking distance and so the overall stopping distance.
1) The tyre tread is important for preventing skidding in wet conditions — so its depth should be checked regularly.

Don't skim read — you might something...

It's so easy to skim read an article given to you in an exam. But don't. Read it really well, underlining or making notes as you go. It's well worth spending some time making sure you understand the article and what the questions are asking for before scribbling down your answers.

Answering Experiment Questions (i)

Science is all (well... a lot) about doing experiments carefully, and interpreting results.
And so that's what they're going to test you on when you do your exam. Among other things.

Read the Question Carefully

Expect at least some questions to describe experiments — a bit like the one below.

Q3 Ellen has three different bottles of citric acid: A, B and C.
The citric acid in each bottle is of a different concentration.

Ellen also has another quantity of citric acid, in the form of kitchen descaler.

Ellen wants to know if any of her three acids are the same concentration as the kitchen descaler. She plans to titrate each of the four citric acid solutions against a solution of sodium hydroxide of a known concentration, as shown.

She repeats the titration 3 times for each acid.

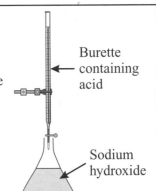

Burette
containing
acid

Sodium
hydroxide

1. What is the independent variable in Ellen's experiment?

   The type of acid used (e.g. A, B or C).

> The <u>independent variable</u> is the <u>thing that the experimenter changes</u> — to see what effect that change has.

> Quite often, experiments involve recording what happens over <u>time</u>, e.g. rate of reaction experiments. In these cases, <u>time</u> is always the <u>independent</u> variable — the experimenter isn't 'changing the time' exactly, but they do want to see what happens <u>as the time changes</u>.

2. What is the dependent variable?

   The quantity of acid required to neutralise the sodium hydroxide.

> The <u>dependent variable</u> is the <u>thing that the experimenter measures</u> (every time they change the independent variable).

3. Give two variables that must be kept the same to make it a fair test.

   1. The amount of NaOH.

   2. The type and amount of indicator used.

> To make it a <u>fair test</u>, you've got to keep <u>all</u> the other variables the same (you're <u>only changing</u> the <u>independent variable</u>). That way you know that the <u>only thing</u> affecting the dependent variable is the <u>independent variable</u>.

4. Give one other precaution that Ellen should take to ensure her results are reliable.

   Wash and dry the equipment each time (to ensure no contamination).

> If your experiment is being done in a <u>lab</u>, this should be fairly easy (though not always — e.g. you might have to keep temperature constant, which could be tricky). But it's <u>trickier</u> still when you don't have much control over the conditions at all — e.g. if your experiment has to be done <u>outside</u> (where temperature, humidity etc. can vary considerably).

Anything that might affect the results needs to be kept constant, so look at the apparatus, think what Ellen's going to be doing — and you should be able to come up with answers fairly easily.

If the equipment isn't <u>clean</u>, that will definitely affect the results. And if the flask's not <u>dry</u>, the extra water would dilute the sodium hydroxide slightly (which would affect the results). A change in temperature could also be a problem (though probably a small one) — things expand as they get hotter, so Ellen could get a false reading from the burette if the temperature in the lab changes drastically between tests.

Answering Experiment Questions (ii)

5. Why did Ellen repeat the titration 3 times for each acid?

   To check for anomalous results and make
   ....
   the results more reliable.
   ....

> Sometimes you get <u>unusual results</u> — <u>repeating</u> an experiment gives you a better idea what the <u>correct result</u> should be.

6. The table below shows the amount of acid required in each titration.

	1st result (cm³)	2nd result (cm³)	3rd result (cm³)	Mean (cm³)
Kitchen descaler	24.1	23.9	23.7	
Acid A	23.9	23.5	24.0	23.8
Acid B	33.3	33.7	(38.6)	33.5
Acid C	23.7	23.9	24.1	23.9

> When an experiment is <u>repeated</u>, the results will usually be <u>slightly different</u> each time.
> To get a single <u>representative</u> value, you'd usually find the <u>mean</u> (average) of all the results.
> The more times the experiment is <u>repeated</u> the <u>more reliable</u> this average will be.
> To find the mean:
> **ADD TOGETHER** all the data values and **DIVIDE** by the total number of values in the sample.
> The <u>range</u> is how <u>spread out</u> the data is.
> You just work out the <u>difference</u> between the <u>highest</u> and <u>lowest</u> numbers.

   a) Calculate the mean amount of kitchen descaler required to neutralise the NaOH.

   Mean = (24.1 + 23.9 + 23.7) ÷ 3 = 23.9 cm³
   ....

   b) What is the range of the quantities of kitchen descaler required?

   24.1 – 23.7 = 0.4 cm³
   ....

> If one result doesn't seem to fit in — it's <u>wildly out</u> compared to all the others — then it's called an <u>anomalous</u> result. You should usually <u>ignore</u> an anomalous result (or even better — investigate it and try to work out what happened). Here, it's been <u>ignored</u> when the mean was worked out.
> This one's a <u>random error</u> — one that only happens occasionally.

7. One of the results on the table is anomalous. Circle the result and suggest why it may have occurred.

   The reading may not have been taken
   ....
   correctly, or the wrong quantity of
   ....
   NaOH may have been used.
   ....

> If you make the same mistake every time, it's a <u>systematic error</u>. For example, if you measured the volume of a liquid using the <u>top</u> of the meniscus rather than the <u>bottom</u>, all your readings would be a little on the large side.

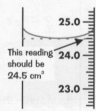

This reading should be 24.5 cm³

8. Using these results, which acid can you conclude is <u>not</u> the same concentration as the kitchen descaler?

   Acid B
   ....

> You have to be careful here — both Acids A and C could be the same concentration, since all experiments have a "margin of error" — meaning results are never absolutely spot on.
> So you can say that Acid B has a different concentration — but Acids A and C could be the same.

We all make mistakes...

No scientist does an experiment just once — unless they like people to point and laugh when the result turns out to be <u>wrong</u>. It's like weightlifting — the more times you repeat an experiment, the better the results will be (unless you're making <u>systematic</u> errors — you'd just have <u>lots</u> of <u>wrong results</u> then).

Answering Experiment Questions (iii)

Use Sensible Measurements for Your Variables

Pu-lin did an experiment to see how the mass of a potato changed depending on the sugar solution it was in.

 She started off by making potato tubes 5 cm in length, 1 cm in diameter and 2.0 g in mass. She then filled a beaker with 500 ml of pure water and placed a potato tube in it for 30 minutes. She repeated the experiment with different amounts of sugar dissolved in the water. For each potato tube, she measured the new mass. She did the experiment using Charlotte, Desiree, King Edward and Maris Piper potatoes.

Before she started, she did a trial run, which showed that most of the potato tubes shrunk to a minimum of 1 g (in a really strong sugar solution) or grew to a maximum of 3 g (in pure water).

1. What kind of variable was the list of potatoes?

   A A continuous variable ○

   B A categoric variable ●

   C An ordered variable ○

   D A discrete variable ○

> Categoric variables are variables that can't be related to size or quantity — they're types of things.
> E.g. names of potatoes or types of fertiliser.

Continuous data is numerical data that can have any value within a range — e.g. length, volume, temperature and time.

Note: You can't measure the exact value of continuous data. Say you measure a height as 5.6 cm to the nearest mm. It's not exact — you get a more precise value if you measure to the nearest 0.1 mm or 0.01 mm, etc.

Ordered variables are things like small, medium and large lumps, or warm, very warm and hot.

Discrete data is the type that can be counted in chunks, where there's no in-between value. E.g. number of people is discrete, not continuous, because you can't have half a person.

2. Pu-lin should add sugar in intervals of...

   A a pinch ○

   B a teaspoon ●

   C a cupful ○

   D a bucketful ○

> It's important to use sensible values for variables.
> It's no good using loads of sugar or really weedy amounts like a pinch at a time cos you'd be there forever and the results wouldn't show any significant difference. (You'd get different amounts of sugar in each pinch anyway.)

3. The balance used to find the mass of the potato should be capable of measuring...

   A to the nearest 0.01 gram ●

   B to the nearest 0.1 gram ○

   C to the nearest gram ○

   D to the nearest 10 grams ○

> A balance measuring only to the nearest gram, or bigger, would not be sensitive enough — the changes in mass are likely to be quite small, so you'd need to measure to the nearest 0.01 gram to get the most precise results.

The sensitivity of an instrument is the smallest change it can detect, e.g. some balances measure to the nearest gram, but really sensitive ones measure to the nearest hundredth of a gram.

For measuring tiny changes — like from 2.00 g to 1.92 g — the more sensitive balance is needed.

You also have to think about the precision and accuracy of your results.

Precise results are ones taken with sensitive instruments, e.g. volume measured with a burette will be more precise than volume measured with a 100 ml beaker. Really accurate results are those that are really close to the true answer. It's possible for results to be precise but not very accurate, e.g. a fancy piece of lab equipment might give results that are precise, but if it's not calibrated properly those results won't be accurate.

I take my tea milky with two bucketfuls of sugar... mmm...

Accuracy, precision and sensitivity are difficult things to get your head around — a sensitive piece of equipment is likely to give precise results (but not necessarily very accurate results). If the equipment is used properly and calibrated well then the results are more likely to be accurate...

Answering Experiment Questions (iv)

Once you've collected all your data together, you need to analyse it to find any relationships between the variables. The easiest way to do this is to draw a graph, then describe what you see...

Graphs Are Used to Show Relationships

These are the results Pu-lin obtained with the King Edward potato.

Number of teaspoons of sugar	0	2	4	6	8	10	12	14	16	18	20
Mass of potato tube (g)	2.50	2.40	2.23	2.10	2.02	1.76	1.66	1.25	1.47	1.3	1.15

4. a) Nine of the points are plotted below.
      Plot the remaining **two** points on the graph.

To plot the points, use a sharp pencil and make a neat little cross.

nice clear mark

smudged unclear marks

   b) Draw a straight line of best fit for the points.

A line of best fit is drawn so that it's easy to see the relationship between the variables. You can then use it to estimate other values.

When drawing a line of best fit, try to draw the line through or as near to as many points as possible, ignoring any anomalous results.

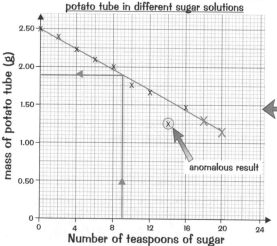

Scattergram to show the mass of a King Edward potato tube in different sugar solutions

anomalous result

This is a scattergram — they're used to see if two variables are related.

This graph shows a negative correlation between the variables. This is where one variable increases as the other one decreases.

The other correlations you could get are:

Positive correlation — this is where as one variable increases so does the other one.

No correlation — this is where there's no obvious relationship between the variables.

5. Estimate the weight of the potato tube if you added nine teaspoons of sugar.

   Estimate of weight = __1.90 g (see graph)__

6. What can you conclude from these results?

   There is a negative correlation between the number of teaspoons of sugar and the mass of potato tube. Each additional teaspoon causes the potato tube to lose mass.

In lab-based experiments like this one, you can say that one variable causes the other one to change. The extra sugar causes the potato to lose mass. You can say this because everything else has stayed the same — nothing else could be causing the change.

There's a positive correlation between revising and good marks...

...really, it's true. Other ways to improve your marks are to practise plotting graphs, and learning how to read them properly — make sure you're reading off the right axis for a start, and don't worry about drawing lines on the graph if it helps you to read it. Always double-check your answer... just in case.

Answering Experiment Questions (v)

A lot of Physics experiments can be done in a <u>nice controlled way</u> in a laboratory. But not all of them. And once you get <u>out of the lab</u> and into the <u>real world</u>, it gets much <u>harder to control</u> all the <u>variables</u>.

Relationships <u>Do</u> NOT <u>Always Tell Us the</u> <u>Cause</u>

On holiday in Scotland, Kate found that mountain streams can be difficult to wade across — the streams flow quite slowly, but there are often many large rocks on the stream bed, which make it difficult to balance.

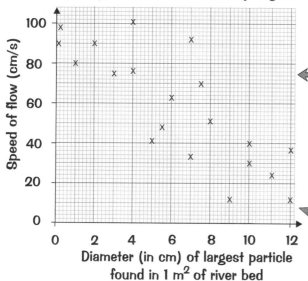

Speed of flow (cm/s) vs Diameter (in cm) of largest particle found in 1 m² of river bed

Kate decided to investigate whether the speed of a river and the size of the rocks/pebbles found on the river bed are related.

She measured the speed of flow and the diameter of the biggest rock/pebble that she found, at several points along the length of one river.

> Outside a lab it can be really <u>difficult</u> to keep conditions the same throughout the study — in this example, if there's a sudden rainstorm in the hills, this will affect the flow of the river.

> In this <u>scattergram</u>, each point plotted represents a different place along the length of the river.

1. What conclusion can you draw from these results?

   The bigger the largest particles on the river bed are, the slower the river tends to be at that point.

> The graph shows a <u>negative correlation</u>. It's not a fantastically <u>strong</u> correlation, but it's definitely there.

> You <u>can't say</u>, just from these results, that <u>bigger particles</u> on the river bed <u>cause</u> the river to slow down. Neither can you say that a <u>slower flow</u> causes bigger particles to collect on the river bed. It could be either way round... or one change might not <u>cause</u> the other at all.

2. Suggest two possible problems with the method Kate has used to describe the size of the particles on the river bed.

   1. Rocks/pebbles aren't usually spherical, so it's hard to say what the 'diameter' is.

   2. The one biggest rock/pebble may be unrepresentative of the others at that point in the river, and so give a misleading result.

> In studies like this where you're unable to control everything, it's possible a <u>third variable</u> is causing the relationship. In this example, the third variable could be something like the width or depth of the river, or the steepness of the slope.

> Try to think of ways the data might be <u>unreliable</u> or the study might be <u>invalid</u>.

Cause and effect — chicken and egg...

It's really hard to prove <u>causation</u>. Think about it — it sounds sensible that a rockier river bed provides more <u>resistance</u> to the flow of water, slowing it down. It sounds just as sensible that as the river slows down, there isn't enough 'oomph' to keep the big rocks bowling along. Which came first? Even if you reckon you <u>know</u> the answer — if your results <u>don't prove it</u>, you <u>can't</u> put it in your conclusion.

Exam Skills

Index

Index

Answers

Revision Summary for Biology 3(i) (page 11)

20) a) The athlete's body will make more red blood cells to compensate for the lower oxygen levels at night. The increased number of red blood cells will allow the athlete to get more oxygen to his or her muscle cells for respiration, meaning more energy is released. This may improve their performance.

b) Live/sleep at a high altitude, e.g. up a mountain. Inject red blood cells.

22) a)

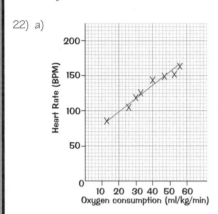

b) It shows that oxygen consumption increases as heart rate increases.

c) When the athlete exercises their muscles consume more oxygen (because they need more energy to contract faster). The heart rate needs to increase in order to supply more oxygen.

Revision Summary for Biology 3(ii) (page 18)

8) Heating yeast to 90 °C for 2 hours kills it. Keeping yeast at 0 °C doesn't kill it. You could repeat your experiment to check if you get the same results.

15) a) Biogas is suitable because waste from the goats and cows can be used in the biogas generator.
Advantages: villagers won't have to spend time collecting wood, digested material could be used to fertilise soil, and waste would be disposed of, reducing disease.
Disadvantages: biogas production slows down in cold conditions, so they might need an alternative fuel source in winter.

b) Their conclusion isn't valid. Possible reasons: the amounts spread on the ground might have been different, the weather in the two places might have been different, the species of crop might have been different etc.

16) a)

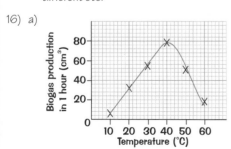

b) 40 °C

c) 44 cm³ in 1 hour so it's 44 × 24 = 1056 cm³ in 24 hours.

Revision Summary for Chemistry 3(i) (page 31)

11) $2Fe_{(s)} + 3Cl_{2(g)} \rightarrow 2FeCl_{3(s)}$

20) Phenolphthalein.

21) a) No. of moles NaOH = 0.2 × (25 ÷ 1000) = 0.005
HCl + NaOH → NaCl + H₂O, so no. of moles HCl = 0.005
Concentration HCl (moles per dm³)
= 0.005 ÷ (49 ÷ 1000) = 0.102 moles per dm³

b) M_r HCl = 1 + 35.5 = 36.5
mass = number of moles × M_r
= 0.102 × 36.5 = 3.72 grams per dm³

22) a) M_r Ca(OH)₂ = 40 + (2 × 16) + (2 × 1) = 74
No. of moles Ca(OH)₂ = mass ÷ M_r = 7.5 ÷ 74 = 0.101 mol
Concentration (moles per dm³) = moles ÷ volume
= 0.101 ÷ 1 = 0.101 moles per dm³

b) Concentration (moles per dm³) = moles ÷ volume
= 0.101 ÷ (100 ÷ 1000) = 1.01 moles per dm³

25) a), c), d), e), g) and i) will all dissolve in water.
b), f) and h) will not dissolve in water.

27) a) 75 g b) 35 °C c) 95 g – 75 g = 20 g

Revision Summary for Chemistry 3(ii) (page 41)

3) a) Mass of water heated = 116 g – 64 g = 52 g
Temperature rise of water = 47 °C – 17 °C = 30 °C
Mass of pentane burnt = 97.72 g – 97.37 g = 0.35 g
So 0.35 g of pentane provides enough energy to heat up 52 g of water by 30 °C.
It takes 4.2 joules of energy to heat up 1 g of water by 1 °C.
Therefore, the energy produced in this experiment is 4.2 × 52 × 30 = 6552 joules.
So, 0.35 g of pentane produces 6552 joules of energy...
... meaning 1 g of pentane produces 6552/0.35
= 18 720 J or 18.720 kJ

8) a) Bonds broken: 2 moles of H–H bonds = 2 × 436 = 872 kJ
1 mole of O=O bonds = 496 kJ
Total energy needed to break bonds = 872 + 496 = 1368 kJ
Bonds made: 2 moles of (2 × O–H bonds) = 2 × 2 × 463
= 1852 kJ
Overall more energy is released than is used,
so 1852 – 1368 = 484 kJ/mol is released.

b) This is an exothermic reaction.

9) 4.2 J = 1 calorie, 655 kJ = 655 000 J
655 000 ÷ 4.2 = 156 000 calories = 156 kcal

17) Mass of carbon = 4.4 × (12 ÷ 44) = 1.2 g
Mass of hydrogen = 1.8 × (2 ÷ 18) = 0.2 g
No. moles carbon = 1.2 ÷ 12 = 0.1 moles
No. moles hydrogen = 0.2 ÷ 1 = 0.2 moles
0.2 ÷ 0.1 = 2 (so there's 1 carbon to every 2 hydrogens)
Empirical formula = CH₂

Revision Summary for Physics 3(i) (page 57)

3) 1.5 × 600 = d × 450, so
d = 900 ÷ 450 = 2 m

14) 3

18) v = 2800 m/s and at the deepest point (B), t = 0.003 s. To find distance travelled to pipe and back, use d = v × t
= 2800 × 0.003 = 8.4 m. So depth of pipe = 8.4 ÷ 2 = 4.2 m

Revision Summary for Physics 3(ii) (page 67)

12) b) The lights go off when the wheel stops turning, e.g. when the cyclist stops at traffic lights

17) $V_s/V_p = N_s/N_p$ so V_s = (600/20) × 9 = 30 × 9 = 270 V